Masters of the Loaded Brush

Oil Sketches from Rubens to Tiepolo

49. Peter Paul Rubens, *Peace Embracing Plenty* (23¾ x 18½ inches). Private Collection.

COLUMBIA UNIVERSITY IN THE CITY OF NEW YORK
DEPARTMENT OF ART HISTORY
AND ARCHAEOLOGY

Masters of the Loaded Brush

Oil Sketches from Rubens to Tiepolo

AN EXHIBITION AT M. KNOEDLER AND COMPANY
14 EAST 57TH STREET, NEW YORK CITY
4 APRIL TO 29 APRIL, 1967

A Benefit Exhibition
for the Scholarship Fund
of the Department of Art History
and Archaeology
of Columbia University
Sponsored by the Advisory Council
of the Department

Under the Gracious Patronage of

Mrs. Lyndon B. Johnson

His Excellency
The Ambassador of Italy
and Mrs. Fenoaltea

His Excellency
The Ambassador of Sweden
and Mrs. de Besche

His Excellency
The British Ambassador
and Lady Dean

His Excellency
The Ambassador of the French Republic
and Mrs. Lucet

Executive Committee

Lenders to the Exhibition

H. M. Queen Elizabeth II
Mr. George Baer
Sig. Andrea Busiri Vici
M. Jean Cailleux
Mrs. Agnes Rindge Claflin
Mr. Brinsley Ford
Mr. and Mrs. Paul Ganz
Mr. and Mrs. Eliot Hodgkin
Mrs. Jacqueline Humphris
Dr. Sonja Binkhorst-Kramarsky
Mrs. Rush Kress
Mr. and Mrs. Milton J. Lewine
Mr. Denis Mahon
Mr. and Mrs. Robert Manning
Sig. Piero Pilati
Mr. and Mrs. David Rust
Mr. Janos Scholz
Mr. and Mrs. Heinrich Schwarz
Mr. Brian Sewell
Sig. M. C. Viezzoli
Mr. and Mrs. John Hay Whitney
Four Anonymous Lenders

Ackland Art Center, University
    of North Carolina
The Albright-Knox Art Gallery,
    Buffalo, New York
The Art Institute of Chicago
The Ashmolean Museum
The Ball State University
    Art Gallery, Muncie, Indiana
The Banca Popolare di Novara
The Cooper Union Museum,
    New York

The Detroit Institute of Arts
The Fogg Art Museum,
    Harvard University
Galleria Nazionale, Rome
Glasgow University
The Los Angeles County Museum
    of Art
The Manchester City Art Galleries
Manufacture Nationale de Sèvres
The Metropolitan Museum of Art
The Minneapolis Institute of Arts
Musée de Picardie, Amiens
Musée des Beaux-Arts, Besançon
Musée des Beaux-Arts, Quimper
Musée des Beaux-Arts, Rouen
Musée des Beaux-Arts, Troyes
Musée du Havre
Musée Grobet-Labadié, Marseille
Museo e Gallerie Nazionali
    di Capodimonte, Naples
Museo Nazionale di S. Martino,
    Naples
Museum of Fine Arts,
    Springfield, Mass.
Nationalmuseum, Stockholm
Pinacoteca di Brera, Milan
Pinacoteca Malaspina, Pavia
Pinacoteca Nazionale, Bologna
The Ponce Art Museum,
    Puerto Rico
Smith College Museum of Art,
    Northampton, Mass.
The Smithsonian Institution
The Wadsworth Atheneum,
    Hartford, Conn.

Notes on the Catalogue

Preface

Following in the tradition of the past Columbia University exhibitions of Great Master Drawings (1959) and of Cézanne Watercolors (1963), the present exhibition is an ambitious enterprise. To our knowledge it has no precedent, for nowhere has there ever been an attempt to demonstrate that there exists an intra-European unity on the level of the oil sketch, a stratum of artistic production of great charm and vitality that seems to have met an ardent response on the part of 19th-century painters.

The choice of pictures was made by a most active and enthusiastic Selection Committee that worked for a year and a half under the benign chairmanship of Winslow Ames. In the course of time many hundred sketches were scrutinized. The final selection was based on a tangle of considerations, but the quality of the sketches was ultimately and primarily the determining factor. During the work of preparation we encountered much good will and cooperation from many sides; and while, regrettably, not all our requests could be granted, particularly that of pictures from the Prado, there is a very great deal to be grateful for.

In the first place we are thankful for Queen Elizabeth II's gracious permission of a loan of works from Windsor Castle and Hampton Court. Mr. Mackworth Young, The Royal Librarian, Miss Aydua Scott-Elliot, Keeper of Drawings at Windsor Castle, and Dr. Oliver Millar, Keeper of the Queen's Pictures, gave us their unstinted support and made the loan possible. I can thank only summarily all the friends, private collectors and staffs of public galleries who helped us cordially in many ways, but I would like to put on record that the difficulties which first seemed to bar the inclusion of an important group of pictures from Italian galleries were overcome by the personal, friendly intervention of His Excellency Ambassador Pio Archi, Director for

xi

Cultural Relations at the Foreign Ministry in Rome, and Professor Bruno Molajoli, Director General of Antiquities and Fine Arts in Rome. Professors Raffaello Causa, Naples, Italo Faldi, Rome, and Cesare Gnudi, Bologna, showed us more than the usual kindness and did everything in their power to make this exhibition a success. In selecting pictures from French museums, we gratefully accepted guidance offered us by MM. Michel Laclotte and Pierre Rosenberg, both of the Department of Paintings in the Louvre. M. Edouard Morot-Sir, Cultural Counselor of French Universities in the United States, and Mme. Danielle Demetz of the Direction des Musées de France paved the way for our successful negotiations with French provincial museums. Professor Fritz Novotny in Vienna earned our gratitude for advising us on loans from Austrian museums, which for a variety of practical reasons could not materialize.

As in the past the exhibition was sponsored by the Advisory Council of the Department of Art History and Archaeology. The members of the Council showed their sustained and inspiring interest on many occasions throughout the long pre-history of the enterprise, and it is they who were ultimately responsible for the choice of the exhibition's topic. We are all particularly grateful to Mr. Peter Grimm, who undertook to raise the funds to underwrite the heavy expenses incurred by the exhibition, and to those members who contributed. At this writing I may particularly mention Mr. and Mrs. John Bass, Mrs. Enid Haupt, Mrs. David M. Heyman, Mrs. Jacob M. Kaplan, Mrs. David Shiverick Smith, and Messrs. Armand Erpf, Henry Ittleson Jr., Edwin C. Vogel, and Arthur Wiesenberger. These ladies and gentlemen and the other members of the Executive Committee were instrumental in making the exhibition, organized for the benefit of the Graduate Students' Scholarship Fund, a financial success. Once again the Executive Committee was co-chaired by Mrs. Grayson Kirk and Mr. Edwin C. Vogel. Both gave us their full support at every stage of the preparation. Mrs. Kirk took on the heavy burden of organizing the Committee and, as before and always, the members of the Department are deeply in her debt.

Once again, the Directors of M. Knoedler and Company and its Chairman, Mr. Roland Balay, offered all their facilities in a most liberal spirit, and Miss Jane Sabersky shared with us many of the long hours of deliberation and allowed us to profit from her wide experience.

The greatest load was on the shoulders of Professor Milton J. Lewine and Miss Sarah Faunce. The former directed the work of the students who wrote the catalogue entries and is responsible for the catalogue; the latter, as Secretary to the Exhibition, revealed infinite resources of patience, ingenuity, and good humor in organizing the entire operation. Without their utter devotion, assisted throughout by Miss Konstanze Bachmann and the office staff of the Department, the exhibition could never have taken place. Finally, the students who participated in the work on the catalogue deserve our gratitude, for many remarkable results of their dedicated research will permanently enrich our store of knowledge.

RUDOLF WITTKOWER, *Chairman*
Department of Art History and Archaeology

Introduction

The present exhibition may well come as a revelation to many visitors. Specialists apart, few lovers of painting have come to realize how rich, diversified and, in a sense, even modern are the oil sketches of the painters of the 17th and 18th centuries. The modern spontaneity and freshness of vision and touch are readily apparent in such pieces as Annibale Carracci's portrait sketch (No. 1), the two small Magnasco studies (31, 32), the remarkable cloud study by Desportes (59), Boucher's *Danaë* (63), and Hogarth's *Ill Effects of Masquerades* (79). It is surely not surprising that the names of Delacroix, Courbet, Renoir, and even such Expressionists as Kokoschka come to mind as we look at these sketches, for the later masters are similar to their forerunners in depending on a virtuoso brushstroke. When Delacroix, the Impressionists, and the Expressionists built up their pictures by a multiplicity of visible strokes of the loaded brush, they did not each time invent afresh a new technique. Rather they adapted a convention with its own long history, and it is the history of this convention to which this exhibition is dedicated.

One of the great revolutions in the history of western painting was due to the specific properties inherent in the oil medium. In contrast to tempera and fresco, oil dries slowly, and it therefore allows a considerable freedom of handling and a free and loose manner. Naturally the painters who first worked with oil used it for the rendering of the same kind of precise forms to which they were accustomed from their work in tempera. But soon artists north and south of the Alps began to discover the magnificent potentialities of the new medium.

Passing over the particular contributions of Jan van Eyck in Bruges and later in the 15th century of the Venetian Giovanni Bellini, the next and decisive step lay with Giorgione at the beginning of the 16th century. He opened entirely new vistas, as his contemporaries were quick to realise, in the way he handled the oil-bearing brush. Vasari, the 16th-century biographer, wrote of Giorgione's *morbidezza,* the softness of his painted surfaces, that resulted from his "working directly with the brush and paint without preliminary drawings," and 17th-century critics praised Giorgione for "the impasto of his soft brush." Giorgione's *alla prima* performance was without precedent, and he was also the first to make use of the coarse-grained canvas for the scintillating effects of the picture, the first to submit color to tonal values, and the first consistently to abandon the firm outlines of depicted forms in favor of a kind of optical blurring. Giorgione's innovations were transcended by Titian who, in his later work, introduced a distinctive brushstroke as the constituent element of a painting. Once again contemporaries fully grasped the significance. Vasari explained that Titian's late pictures "are carried out with thick brushstrokes and color blobs in such a way that one cannot see them (i.e., the pictures) from a near standpoint, while they look perfect from a distance." Venetian painters—for example Schiavone, Jacopo Bassano and above all Tintoretto—immediately followed Titian's lead, thereby popularising the new way of painting in Venice and the Terra Ferma. And this new technique of working with bold brushstrokes and patches of color, called by Italians *pittura di tocco e di macchia,* was also described in the 16th and 17th centuries by many writers other than Vasari, thus giving international circulation to the new mode of painting and, as is clearly implied in Vasari's words, to the new mode of perception.

Although painting with the loaded brush originated in Venice, it was more than a local exploitation of the inherent potentialities of the oil medium and was even more than Titian's private and ingenious response to a new psychology of vision. The rapid stroke that reveals the hand of the artist at work was in fact an answer to an intellectual revolution of the first order. The modern artist, as a self-reliant and independent gentleman who belonged to the intellectual élite, was born in 16th-century Italy when artists spiritually—if not always in fact—fulfilled their dream of freedom from guild-controlled artisanship. Pedantic execution of a work smacks of the artisan's craft, and Vasari was appalled by the dry and labored performances of 15th-century artists. The modern artist had to perform in a way that matched his new status, and so all contemporary theoreticians insisted on facility of execution as an essential requirement of the good painter. For his *Dialogue on Painting* (1557), Lodovico Dolce borrowed his terminology from the Renaissance text-book for gentlemanly demeanor, Castiglione's *Courtier,* and stated clearly that the up-to-date artist was to display *sprezzatura;* this was the term coined by Castiglione for the easy and effortless manner to be shown in all human activity. But contemporaries also argued that artistic facility cannot be attained without toil. As Francisco de Hollanda explained in his *Dialogues,* purporting to be a record of conversations with Michelangelo: it needs extraordinary skill to make works look as though they had been done rapidly and effortlessly when indeed much labor had been spent on them. Nevertheless the rule was clear; Dolce advised that under all circumstances too careful precision must be avoided.

Facility cannot be achieved without natural talent and its concomitants, inspiration and spontaneity. To us this is a hackneyed truism, but to acknowledge it and see it in relation to the creative process needed a long germinating period. In 1550, however, Vasari ventured to say: "Many painters . . . achieve in the first sketch of their work, as though guided by a sort of fire of inspiration . . . a certain measure of boldness: but afterwards, in finishing it, the boldness vanishes." In other words, Vasari noticed that the quick touch, an apparent sign of facility, was all too often limited to the initial stage of creation. The artists, of course, were always aiming at a finished picture, and few among them or of the public were ready to regard the preparatory exercises as works in their own right. But Vasari's memorable remark would seem to open a re-evaluation of these preparatory stages, and Vasari himself collected drawings, including an oil sketch on paper by Tintoretto, and valued the sketch-like unfinished pictures of Parmigianino. Yet in fact it took a long time before a wider public accorded the preparatory sketch the high place claimed for it in Vasari's thoughtful observation.

Our concern here is the history and 'anatomy' of the oil sketch, a special case within the process of preparation. Following Giorgione,

Titian in his late works painted *alla prima,* straight on the canvas, and, although he continued to develop his works in slow stages, the final picture retained something of the basic character of magnified oil sketches. One would like to think that the small oil sketch grew out of such a painterly procedure, but history is rarely tidy. While an oil sketch by Titian is documented for 1540, Polidoro da Caravaggio made a few in the 1530's and Lotto and Beccafumi apparently produced occasional oil sketches, primarily of heads. Nevertheless the whole course of Venetian painting predestined Venice to develop the oil sketch as a regular part of the preparatory process. The first such oil sketches can probably be associated with Tintoretto. Other Venetians followed; and in the last decades of the 16th century oil sketches were well established in Venice and had begun to exert their appeal beyond its borders.

A great number of boldly executed oil monochromes on paper were made in Tintoretto's studio, mostly executed by Tintoretto's son Domenico, and this technique, in less sketchy form, was taken up in Bologna in the Carracci circle after about 1585. The last decades of the 16th century were fertile years for experimentation, and the Venetian idea of oil sketches on paper as well as on canvas, in monochrome as well as in rich colors, soon found a warm welcome in other North Italian centers, particularly in Milan and Genoa. The work of the Milanese group—Cerano, Morazzone, Giulio Cesare Procaccini, and Tanzio—is rich in oil sketches at an early date. A great masterpiece of this group is here on view (30), while the Genoese are represented by Strozzi (26), Valerio Castello (27), and G. B. Castiglione (28, 29), the latter's technical innovations transcending the boundaries of drawing, water color, and oil sketch. Florence, Rome and Naples were at first less receptive to oil-sketch preparations, but even before the turn of the century such Florentines as Cristofano Allori and Lodovico Cigoli created spirited oil sketches that reveal Tintoretto's influence. On the whole, it would seem that in the great central and southern Italian centers of art the painters who had Venetian contacts —such as Mola (8, 9), Gaulli (13), Pozzo (14), Preti (21), Luca Giordano (22), and Solimena (24)—were more devoted to this form of creation than their less mobile or less adventurous compatriots.

The 17th and 18th centuries were the age of the full flowering of academies of art, guardians of a rationalizing theory and practice focused on design rather than color. During this time the rank and file of artists embraced whole-heartedly the Renaissance method of careful preparation: one began with sketches for the composition and studies from nature, developed a meticulously executed final design by stages, and lastly produced a cartoon that was painstakingly used for the execution of the picture. Within this established pattern there was hardly room for the spirited oil sketch and, in the case of academically oriented artists, for the play of the loaded brush in the finished work. It is not surprising that Rome, which in the 17th century harbored within its walls both Bernini's dynamic baroque art (6) and a strongly classicist current, had a less vigorous oil-sketch production than did other centers. Nevertheless even such classicising artists as Sacchi (7) found room in their preparatory work for oil sketches, and by the end of the century and throughout the 18th century they became a normal part of the procedure of Roman artists (8–19).

But one will notice that in their oil sketches few Roman painters attained a freedom comparable with that of the Venetians. The great period of the Venetian oil sketch was of course the 18th century when the Venetian school blossomed into an unequalled late flowering (38–46). In contrast to many Romans, the Venetians, continuing and broadening their 16th-century tradition, imparted the virtuoso brushstroke of the sketch to the finished picture. It is for this reason that true oil sketches are extremely rare in the works of some Venetian and North Italian artists such as Guardi (46) or Magnasco (31, 32), while others, such as Marco Ricci, may never have executed any.

The Venetian oil-sketch tradition also spread north of the Alps. As a court-painter at Mantua, the young Rubens lived for a time within the Venetian orbit, and it is a fair assumption that his interest in oil sketches was then awakened. His own reliance on the preparatory oil sketch grew over the years, and all his great cycles of the 1620's and '30's were primarily prepared in oil sketches (47–50). His example inspired other northern artists, and the exhibition includes two magnificent oil sketches by Van Dyck (53, 54) and one by Jordaens (51).

In France, Lebrun, the master-mind of Louis XIV's grandiose enterprises who owed his artistic formation to his four years' stay in Italy, made ample use of oil sketches (56). When the academic structure of French art began to break up around 1670, the new spirit became manifest in a growing admiration for Venetian painting and in the exaltation of Rubens, the colorist *par excellence,* at the expense of Poussin, the classicist idol of the French Academy. Charles de La Fosse, a determined 'Rubenist' who had spent years in Rome and Venice, displays his attachment to Italian models in the sketch here shown (57), although still painted in the allegorical court-style of Louis XIV. In 1699 La Fosse was elected Director of the Paris Academy, and the way was open for the free and glorious development of French painting in the 18th century (59–72). The exhibition contains superb examples of the vigorous brushwork in the sketches of Boucher, Fragonard, de Troy, Greuze, and of some less well-known masters—Desportes, Barbault, and Vien from among the many who could have been added—, demonstrating that the spirited oil sketch had become a universally practiced art form. Germany, Austria, and England welcomed such Italian artists as Carloni (33, 34) and Pellegrini (40), active producers of oil sketches, and the few examples on view of sketches by native artists indicate not only that there were no national barriers in this field but that painters like Maulbertsch, Sigrist or Hogarth (74, 75, 78, 79) were at times capable of a sublime boldness of idiosyncratic presentation hardly ever matched in France or Italy.

We must now turn to what I have called the anatomy of the oil sketch because obviously oil sketches were not all undertaken for the same reasons. Historical scrutiny shows that we can differentiate between at least five different types:

(i). The spontaneous oil sketch: the first fixing of a picture's composition and color; the oil sketch may remain the only preparation or may be further developed in drawings.

(ii). The oil sketch as clarifying statement: a complete idea of the carefully deliberated formal and color composition, based on drawings and made for the artist's own use.

(iii). The oil sketch as model ('modello'): a small sketch executed with considerable care for the patron, to give him as full an idea as possible of the appearance of the projected final version.

(iv). The oil sketch *post festum:* a small version of the finished picture painted by the artist or an assistant, either to be kept in the studio ('ricordo') or to be sold (reduced replica or version).

(v). The autonomous oil sketch: a picture in its own right, divorced from the preparatory process and without sequel; it may be a rapid copy after another artist's work, a study after nature, or an independent composition.

In actual fact the oil sketches themselves often defy easy labeling or categorization: the spontaneous sketch (i), the clarifying sketch (ii), and the autonomous sketch (v) are all usually called 'bozzetti'; a modello (iii) may look like a spontaneous sketch (i) or vice versa; a modello and a ricordo (iv) are anyway so close in character that without documentation they are sometimes indistinguishable. In many cases a sketch appears autonomous (v) simply because we are unaware of a final picture. The variables are endless, but with this proviso for error, we may claim to have most types of oil sketch represented in the exhibition. The bulk, however, are true preparatory sketches or bozzetti (i and ii). These command the greatest interest, both as documents of the creative process and as displays of a brilliant lightness of touch, as a rule surpassing that of modelli and ricordi. Often we know the final picture to which a sketch relates or can posit its existence. Among the sketches here on display are some of extraordinary rarity, such as the unique bozzetti by Crespi (4) and Cavallino (20) and the puzzling Canaletto (45). Not infrequently we know of more than one oil sketch for the same work. In the case of Gaulli (13) two different stages of clarifying oil sketches have come down to us, while in the case of Cades (19, 19A) there survive the first spontaneous bozzetto, a clarifying sketch and the modello. In the exhibition can also be studied the striking difference that may exist between a spontaneous sketch and those that clarify ideas, a difference revealed, for instance, if the unusually temperamental performances of Pellegrini (40) and Hogarth (78, 79) are compared with Lebrun's more deliberate study (56). On the other hand the sketches by Subleyras (17) and Piazzetta (41) may be either bozzetti or modelli; a decision is especially difficult in the case of the Neapolitans whose tradition favored detailed oil sketches (De Mura, 25). Nor do we know whether the sketch by Sacchi here shown (7) is a modello or ricordo. Sebastiano Ricci's work (38) is, however, surely a modello, and we are fortunate in having in the exhibition what is perhaps the grandest modello ever painted, Pozzo's outsize sketch for the vault of the nave of S. Ignazio in Rome (14). The greatest masters of the oil sketch, Rubens and Tiepolo, are represented here by some splendid works, but to illustrate their range fully one would have had to show many more. Two of Rubens's sketches (47, 48) are clarifying studies (ii) as well as modelli (iii), while one by Tiepolo (42) may be an autonomous bozzetto. In this latter category probably also belong the portrait studies by Annibale Carracci (1), Bernini (6), and Fragonard (71, 72) and the compositional sketches by Mola (8, 9), Magnasco (31, 32), Bazzani (35, 36), Guardi (46), and Barbault (65).

A valid test for what constitutes an autonomous oil sketch cannot be given. The words 'sketch' and 'bozzetto' refer to the preliminary state of a design, however rough or detailed. Thus apparently by definition no oil sketch can be autonomous. Yet this logic is fallacious. We have already noted that at a certain moment in history the sketchy picture, rapidly executed with bold brushstrokes, was accorded full rights as a finished work, and the difference between a large picture of this kind and an autonomous oil sketch is basically one of size. Indeed, it boils down to the question of the artist's intent whether a small or tiny sketchy picture, designated by us as oil sketch or bozzetto, was meant to be a 'finished' work or not. Who can decide where the format of a bozzetto ends and that of a picture begins? And yet there is perhaps something more to this problem. A large picture was as a rule made for a patron, placing the artist under definite obligations with regard to durability and 'readability'. Before the 19th century almost all paintings, even if worked *alla prima,* were underpainted and then further developed, on principle following Titian's method. It was only in his spontaneous sketch, often though not always done without consideration of the patron, that an artist could develop a degree of freedom that was attainable in the large picture only under very special conditions.

This freedom pertains, of course, also to our categories (i) and (ii), and it is precisely the unmatched freedom of handling in the oil sketches of many 17th and 18th century artists that is historically so significant and visually so attractive to the modern eye. Just as we enjoy drawings for their own sake, we are inclined to appreciate these oil sketches as autonomous works of art, disregarding their artists' original intention and their patrons' way of seeing and judging.

It is difficult to ascertain when small oil sketches were first intended as autonomous pictures. Roberto Longhi recently suggested that the beginnings lay in Parmigianino and Beccafumi. But the evidence is shaky, and it seems more likely that we should find the earliest autonomous bozzetti in Venice, where Vasari credited Tintoretto with such works "handled with fortuitous and fiercely rough brushstrokes." Although autonomous oil sketches were certainly created by masters of the 17th century, their real time came in the 18th century when the borderline between the oil sketch and the small picture tended to become blurred (Guardi, 46). Only then did it become more common to concede to both the painter's sketch in oil and the sculptor's bozzetto in terracotta the status of works of art in their own right.

To take up such a position showed a high degree of sophistication on the part of connoisseurs. Rapid oil sketches made even greater demands on sensibility and understanding than did the paintings of the 16th-century masters of the loaded brush; and it needed infinitely more active collaboration on the part of the spectator to 'decipher' a sketch by Magnasco (31, 32) than a painting by Domenichino or a Bolognese academician, worked with firm outlines and a smooth surface. The 18th-century 'virtuoso', or trained amateur, formed the nucleus of a small public. Keyed up to an aesthetic approach, he could savor the specific qualities and characteristics of each master, even associating hands with individual peculiarities of the brushstroke, and find in the oil sketch or the terracotta bozzetto equal or perhaps greater merits than in the finished product. Already in the mid-17th century the Venetian critic Boschini extolled the virtues of the masters of the rapid and bold brushstroke in terms never heard before. In the further course of the 17th century discussion of how to distinguish hands stylistically grew fast, and criteria were more and more subtly differentiated. Artistic facility, so highly valued from the second half of the

16th century onwards, was now regarded as synonymous with rapidity, and an artist like Schiavone, censured by 16th-century critics—even by the admirers of the *pittura di tocco*—because of the swiftness of his production, came in for exalted praise. Luca Giordano (22) carried his nickname *fa presto* (quick worker), given to him in his youth, like a title of honor. In his *Essay on the Theory of Painting* of 1715, the English painter and critic Jonathan Richardson confessed his love for the freedom of painting and for the small sketch handled with "bold rough touches"; he regarded it as almost impossible to preserve the spirit and beauty of the quick sketch in the more finished work: we are reminded of Vasari's prophetic words. Richardson concluded that it was better "to incur the censure of the injudicious than to hazard the losing such advantages"—an indication that despite the agreement of scores of critics such as Padre Resta, Dézailler d'Argenville and Mariette, the public at large was still incapable of appreciating the specific qualities of sketches.

Oil sketches were appreciated as works of art when they became collectors' items. Many 18th-century collectors are on record, particularly from the end of the century, who liked to surround themselves with bozzetti and modelli, but in an earlier period such collectors were few. Occasionally sketches were sought out in the first half of the 17th century, but among early collectors the palm must go to the almost forgotten Cardinal Leopoldo de' Medici (1617–75), the youngest son of Grand Duke Cosimo II, a richly endowed man with a deep love for the sciences, literature, and art who deserves to be honored as the founder of the Uffizi collection of drawings and of artists' self-portraits. He was also an avid collector of oil sketches, and it is probably not too much to say that he awakened a taste for them in a coterie of connoisseurs. His collection survives, housed in rooms in the Palazzo Pitti, closed to the public and shown only once in recent years, at the Palazzo Strozzi in 1952. His example was followed by his great-nephew Grand Prince Ferdinando (1664–1713), Florence's greatest collector, whose love for Venetian painting, for pictures with strong impasto, for oil sketches and modelli led to the amassing in Florence of unimaginable treasures of works painted with the loaded brush.

By then oil sketches had definitely been singled out as works of the highest class. They were appreciated by art lovers of the following generations and were carefully studied by artists, for whom they became a rich fund of inspiration. Cézanne once expressed his love for Tintoretto's work, ending his train of thought with the reflection that artists "turn towards the admirable works that have been handed down to us through the ages; they give us comfort and the support that a plank gives to the bather."

RUDOLF WITTKOWER

Index of Artists

Catalogue

Italy

BOLOGNA

ANNIBALE CARRACCI (1560–1609)

Annibale Carracci, born in Bologna, first studied under his cousin Lodovico. With Annibale's older brother, Agostino, the three Carracci shared a workshop and established an informal academy in 1582. Annibale visited Parma between 1580 and 1585 to study Correggio, and probably Venice in about 1586–7 where the great 16th-century masters, above all Titian and Veronese, attracted him. Annibale's work of the late 1580's and early 1590's reflects strong Venetian influence. From 1595 to 1605 he was active in Rome, notably on the frescoes in the Palazzo Farnese. To his earlier training Annibale added the study of antiquity, Raphael and Michelangelo to form a grand classical manner that had a lasting influence on the further history of painting. As in his early Bolognese days, he continued in Rome to paint informal pictures, particularly landscapes and genre scenes. In the last years of his life he succumbed to severe melancholia and rarely painted.

1. *HEAD OF A MAN IN PROFILE.* Oil on canvas. 17⅝ x 12⅝ inches (44.8 x 32.1 cm). Inscribed lower left: *118* (inventory number of 1858). COLLECTION: King George III. EXHIBITION: *Italian Art and Britain,* Royal Academy, London, 1960, No. 121. LITERATURE: C. H. Collins Baker, *Catalogue of the Pictures at Hampton Court,* Glasgow, 1929, No. 294; R. Longhi, "Uno sguardo alle fotografie della Mostra 'Italian Art and Britain'," *Paragone,* XI, 1960, No. 125, p. 60 (with incorrect reference to No. 148); M. Levey, *The Later Italian Pictures in the Collection of Her Majesty the Queen,* London, 1964, No. 435.

This vividly sketched portrait shows the head and shoulders of a man in profile, with an arched nose, high forehead, thick brown hair, moustache, whiskers and beard, dressed in a black coat with a red cravat

3

and a limp, frilled white collar. The sketch, recorded in an 1818 Royal inventory as by Titian (Levey, No. 435), has been attributed to Sebastiano Ricci (Collins Baker, No. 294) and was exhibited as by that artist at the Royal Academy in 1960 along with another study of a man. Longhi noted that the latter study was copied from Veronese's *Feast in the House of Levi* in Venice; the seven heads by Ricci at Hampton Court (Levey, Nos. 629–635) are similar copies after Veronese. (Ricci repeatedly included these in his own versions of Veronese's religious paintings.) The head in this exhibition, however, cannot be found in Veronese's *oeuvre*. Longhi regarded it as a study from life by the young Annibale, *circa* 1585, and the attribution has gained general acceptance.

The sketch is an example of Annibale's Venetian or neo-Venetian manner, datable between 1588 and 1595. He may have gone to Venice himself, but Agostino had certainly made the trip in 1582 and brought back to Bologna ideas he had learned in the studios of the Bassani and Tintoretto.

Annibale's portrait drawings belong to the Bolognese and early Roman periods. Studies from life, they are often drawn in black and red chalk, painterly in style and close to the Venetian tradition. A fine example, and one that lends itself for comparison with our bozzetto, is the portrait drawing of Baldassare Aloisi, called il Galanino, inscribed *Annibale Ca . . . in Bo . . . 159 . . .* (1590?; D. Mahon, *Mostra dei Carracci: Disegni*, Bologna, 1956, No. 219, pl. 72). Reference may also be made to the neo-Venetian male portrait in Munich and the Uffizi self-portrait of *circa* 1595 (*Mostra*, Nos. 70, 75), both of which support the attribution of our sketch. Annibale's 17th-century biographer, Malvasia, criticized the looseness of the latter portrait, painted *nel modo sprezzato e vile*, but this sketchy manner is just what is so highly prized today and is readily apparent in our sketch.

It is difficult to determine whether this and other painted portrait sketches by Annibale were meant to be complete in themselves or studies from life made for his own enjoyment and practice or preparatory to more finished versions. It was not uncommon for Annibale to prepare his work by oil studies on paper, canvas and panel. Future research may well uncover additional portrait sketches in oil and resolve their problems of attribution and function.   M.L.G.

Lent by gracious permission of Her Majesty Queen Elizabeth II, from Hampton Court Palace

GIUSEPPE MARIA CRESPI (1665–1747)

Giuseppe Maria Crespi, who was born in Bologna and almost never left it, absorbed all the currents of his city's traditions by copying frescoes in S. Michele in Bosco (1680–2) and by studying with Canuti (1682–4) and Cignani (1684–6). By 1690 Crespi had developed a spirited and independent style of his own. He stood at the opposite pole from the academic painter Franceschini. His patrons were mainly princes, popes and cardinals, but his fame rested on his ability to deal with pleasing subjects of low-keyed, middle-class humor and pathos. He was perhaps the most northern of Italian painters, combining an intense sensitivity for the vagaries of light with an eagerness to record the tender aspects of common life. An invaluable biography of him was written by his son Luigi (in C. Malvasia, *Felsina Pittrice* . . . , Rome, 1769, III, pp. 201 ff.)

2. *BLIND BEGGAR.* Oil on canvas. 14⅜ x 10⅝ inches (36.3 x 27 cm). COLLECTION: Private collection, Milan. LITERATURE: A. Riccoboni, "Inediti del seicento bolognese," *Emporium,* CXXXIII, 1961, pp. 104–5.

Lent by Sig. Piero Pilati, Bologna

3. *PEASANT SCENE WITH STREET MUSICIANS.* Oil on canvas, lined. 18⅝ x 12¾ inches (48 x 32 cm). COLLECTION: Sankt Lucas Gallery, Vienna, 1937. EXHIBITIONS: *Italienische Barockmalerei,* Galerie Sankt Lucas, Vienna, 1937, No. 31; *Exhibition of Italian Baroque Painting of the 17th and 18th Centuries,* Vassar College Art Gallery, 1940, No. 9; *Art of the Past,* Addison Gallery of American Art, Phillips Academy, Andover, Mass., 1944, No. 35; *Exhibition of Italian Baroque Painting, 17th and 18th Centuries,* Smith College Museum of Art, Northampton, Mass., 1947, No. 16. LITERATURE: T. C. Howe Jr., "Variety in the Work of Giuseppe Maria Crespi," *Pacific Art Review,* I, 2, 1941, pp. 3–4.

Lent by Mrs. Agnes Rindge Claflin, Brooklyn, New York

Scenes of Bolognese street life fascinated Crespi. To observe them he constructed a species of *camera oscura,* using an aperture in his door through which he recorded the lowly activities in the small courtyard of the working-class neighborhood in which he lived (Luigi Crespi, p. 218). He was uninterested in preparatory drawings, and not a single certain one survives, although sources tell us that he did do some early in his career. More commonly, Crespi painted small canvases with single figures observed from life, which he then inserted, sometimes in a pastiche fashion, into his more complex works. This is the case with the woman suckling a baby here, for which there exists a small oil sketch (Private Collection, Bologna), used again in the famous Budapest *Farm Family*. Despite the evidence that the *Street Musicians* is a constructed scene, Crespi succeeded here in invoking an image of a passing incident recorded quickly and spontaneously with all the accidents of gesture and light.

The apparent intense preoccupation with the effects of limited light helps date these paintings in the years of the *Seven Sacraments* (Dresden), signed and dated 1712. Luigi writes that it was a sudden vision of the confessional, spotlighted by a ray of light filtering through a window in one of Bologna's dark churches, that caused Crespi to borrow a confessional and draft his friend Lodovico Mattioli to play the part of the penitent. (This is an invaluable recollection of the genesis of Crespi's major work, previsioning the methods of the French Impressionists.) And it is light again that is the primary subject in these two sketches, light as revealed by single touches of a brilliantly controlled brush. A cheek, a hand, the curve of a leg, or the roundness of a forehead gleam in a murky, brown atmosphere.

The sources for Crespi's choices of subject matter and treatment are not easily definable. Unlike other Italian genre painters—Monsù Bernardo, Pasquale Rossi, Todeschini, and Jacopo Ceruti—Crespi did not paint large half-figure compositions of types tangential to society, nor did he handle his common folk as a merciless observer feeding a compassionless curiosity. The affinity of Crespi's themes to that of the Dutch masters, especially Rembrandt, whose early etchings gave precedent for subject matter based on street life, has frequently been noted. Yet even in Bologna an incipient tradition of such themes existed already in the 17th century with the Carracci and more contemporaneously with G. M. Mitelli, corresponding more closely to Crespi's sensibility. As the two sketches indicate, this sensibility, incapable of Rembrandt's uncompromising scrutiny of age, loneliness, and decay, was expressed in a sentimental idealization (in this Crespi was to the end Bolognese) that is chastened by a tinge of knavery and redeemed by a poetic sympathy for the characters.

If Rembrandt's etchings, which Luigi informs us his father tried to emulate, did in fact lead Crespi to new iconographic possibilities handled in light and dark, we must conclude that Rembrandt's language was not only italianized in Crespi's hands but was also transfigured by a trace of levity, which the sources often assure us informed so many of Crespi's attitudes and actions. M.P.M.

4. *MARTYRDOM OF ST. PETER OF ARBUÉS.* Oil on paper, lined. 16½ x 11 inches (42 x 28 cm). Restored and cleaned in 1966. LITERATURE: E. Mauceri, *La Regia Pinacoteca di Bologna,* Rome, 1935, pp. 151-2; for other late martyrdom pictures, see E. Modigliani, "Dipinti inediti del Crespi, 'Lo Spagnolo,' " *Dedalo,* IV, 1923-24, p. 415 ff.

Luigi Crespi tells us that the last large history painting his father executed was the altarpiece in the Collegio di Spagna in Bologna (Pl. 4A) for which this is a bozzetto. It can be dated between 1733 and 1738 because it is not mentioned in Zanotti's manuscript of his *Storia dell' Accademia Clementina,* datable *circa* 1733, but does appear in the published work of 1739. The painting was commissioned by Cardinal Lambertini, later Pope Benedict XIV, to replace an earlier altarpiece that apparently treated the same subject—the martyrdom of a Spanish priest, once a student in Bologna and now a member of the Inquisition in Aragon, who was killed by enraged Jewish converts while praying in church.

This bozzetto has the unusual distinction of being the only direct preparatory sketch for a large commission that survives in Crespi's *œuvre,* thus offering a unique opportunity for examining Crespi's development of a pictorial idea. One can see, for instance, that certain qualities of Crespi's late style, sometimes called mannerisms of a tired painter, were actually deliberately sought effects. These focus his increasing interest in the energy available to evil-doers engaged in despoiling or destroying the pure and the innocent. Themes of the violence done to Christ and the saints multiply disproportionately during Crespi's late years and, as the bozzetto reveals, he very consciously brutalized the torturers in the transition between the instinctive bozzetto and the reworked altarpiece. For instance, the proportions of the attackers, in the bozzetto long and slender, become in the final work squat and burly; in the former the legs and feet are covered by inconspicuous dark clothing, in the latter Crespi unclothed and enlarged them, as well as the hands and the arms, so as to put emphasis on their aggressive function as they grab, tear and kick the saint. The altar, placed at an angle and to the side in the sketch, is lowered and turned more into the plane in the finished work, thus squeezing the action into a limited space so that it becomes much more explosive.

Crespi's dark style of the 1730's, with its crushing concentration on piety confronted by evil, can be seen as the last remnant of counter-reformatory expression, contrasting with the idyllic classicism of his Bolognese contemporaries. Examined on its own merits, Crespi's late manner seems the result of a disturbed awareness of the tangibility of the beast in mankind. And since Crespi expressed this awareness by means of emotional light and loose brush, his work may also be seen as an isolated and early adumbration of much later developments in Spain and France, particularly in the art of Goya.   M.P.M.

Lent by the Pinacoteca Nazionale di Bologna

GAETANO GANDOLFI (1734–1802)

Born in Matteo della Decima near Bologna, Gandolfi was the pupil of his older brother Ubaldo (1728–1781) and of Ercole Lelli in Bologna. He made a trip to Venice with Ubaldo in 1760 and was apparently influenced by G. B. Tiepolo and other Venetians. He then returned to Bologna where in 1767 he was elected a member of the Accademia Clementina. Except for a short trip to London between 1787 and 1788, Gandolfi worked mainly in Bologna. He painted numerous religious and profane subjects, as well as portraits, but was known especially for his large fresco decorations. His earliest known works date from the 1750's.

5. *RAPE OF GANYMEDE.* Oil on canvas. 15 x 19½ inches (38.5 x 50 cm). COLLECTION: Giovanni Ceschi, Bologna. EXHIBITION: *Mostra della pittura italiana del seicento e del settecento,* Palazzo Pitti, Florence, 1922, No. 437; *Mostra del settecento bolognese,* Bologna, 1935, No. 24; *Seventeenth and Eighteenth Century Italian Paintings,* Hazlitt Gallery, London, 1963, No. 12; *Art Historians and Critics as Collectors,* Thos. Agnew & Sons, Ltd., London, 1965, No. 41. LITERATURE:

U. Ojetti *et al.*, *La pittura italiana del seicento e del settecento alla mostra di Palazzo Pitti*, Milan-Rome, 1924, p. 134; L. Bianchi, *I Gandolfi*, Rome, 1936, pp. 70–72.

This canvas shows the abduction of Ganymede, the Trojan youth who was taken from the earth to become cup-bearer for the gods (*Iliad*, XX, 232). According to some versions, Zeus himself, disguised as an eagle, carried off the adolescent (Ovid, *Metamorphoses*, X, 155 ff), while in others Zeus and his eagle appear together to capture the boy. Hera, identifiable by her peacock, has also been included here, probably as a disapproving onlooker; two putti holding crowns stand behind her.

The oval shape of the composition and the angular viewpoint make it clear that this free and airy sketch was made in connection with a ceiling decoration for a house or villa. The ceiling, however, is not known. According to Bianchi (p. 156, No. 61), another oil sketch of the same subject, of the same height but narrower, exists in a private collection in Bologna and reproduces the London sketch with only minor variations.

Bianchi dated the sketch *circa* 1763 and claimed that it was executed in the local Bolognese style despite the fact that Gaetano had recently returned from Venice. The sketch does indeed show the gentle classicism of Bologna but, nevertheless, Venetian influence is evident here, both in composition and in the forms. The *Ganymede* recalls, for example, such a fresco by G. B. Tiepolo as *La forza dell'eloquenza* in the Palazzo Sandi in Venice (see especially the Orpheus and Eurydice group, in Morassi, *Tiepolo*, 1955, fig. 10), and for the Tiepolesque character of the sketch in general, one can even compare it with the Tiepolo sketches on exhibition here (Nos. 43, 44). But Gaetano was able to transform the ideas of Tiepolo into a personal language, and the ease and elegance of the sketch are his own.   s.b.s.

Lent by Mr. Brinsley Ford, London

ROME

Attributed to GIAN LORENZO BERNINI (1598–1680)

Bernini was born in Naples, the son of a sculptor who moved the family to Rome in 1604, and he lived and worked there throughout his life but for a brief visit in 1665 to Paris, at the request of Louis XIV. As a sculptor and architect, he transformed the city of Rome, and his influence was international, enduring over three generations. He was also a poet and a painter who, early in his career, produced over 200 pictures, but few of these are known today. The attributions, almost all of them of heads, are recent, and most of them have turned up bearing the names of Sacchi, Velazquez or Murillo.

6. *A BOY SINGING.* Oil on paper, mounted on canvas. Damaged: holes at the right and roughened edges. 10¹⁄₁₆ x 9⅜ inches (25.5 x 23.8 cm). EXHIBITION: *The Hunterian Collection,* Kenwood, London, 1952, No. 10 (as Italian School, mid-17th century). LITERATURE (all as Andrea Sacchi): Sir Robert Strange, *A Descriptive Catalogue.* . . , 1769, No. 62; J. Laskey, *A General Account of the Hunterian Collection, Glasgow,* Glasgow, 1813, No. 29; J. Dennistoun, *Memoirs of Sir Robert Strange and . . . Andrew Lumsden,* London, 1855, II, p. 180.

This sketch, vigorously painted in brown and white on paper, has nothing to do with Sacchi, under whose name it turned up in the 18th century. Instead it belongs in type, lighting, and expression to an artist working in Rome after the 1610's in the manner of Caravaggio: characteristic of the time and place is the combination we see here of Caravaggio's dramatic lighting of his late Roman style coupled with a taste for genre that is indebted to his earlier manner. One seeks in vain to place the sketch in the style of any of Caravaggio's immediate following, from the great Valentin de Boulogne to the minor Pietro Paolini, but the intense concentration of energy and the sureness of the rapid brushstroke demand a name of high calibre. And the name of Bernini, recently suggested by Rudolf Wittkower, must inevitably come to mind. Bernini's portraits, dating mainly from the 1620's and the early 1630's, show a vigorous brushwork not found among the Caravaggio succession, an animated turn of the head, a direct gaze at the viewer, and an open mouth as though the sitter were about to speak. Such elements of vitality and animation are present here, and the dropped jaw of the boy recalls Bernini's early *Damned Soul*. The striking parallels suggest that Bernini was responsible for this sketch, made in his youth (*circa* 1620) when he eagerly absorbed all he could learn from all the great Roman masters whose works he encountered.   M.L.G.

Lent by Glasgow University, Hunterian Collection

ANDREA SACCHI (1599–1661)

Born in Rome, Sacchi trained there and in Bologna *ca.* 1616–1620 with Francesco Albani and worked in Rome all his life. His reputation was established by his *Miracle of St. Gregory the Great* painted for St. Peter's in 1624–5. From 1629 onwards he worked almost exclusively for the Barberini family and their immediate circle. After the death of Urban VIII (1644), and the subsequent disgrace of the Barberini, Sacchi lacked steady patronage. His rate of production fell off, and when in 1653 Cardinal Antonio Barberini the Younger returned to Rome from Paris, Sacchi failed to complete any of several important commissions the cardinal gave him. His most talented pupil was Carlo Maratti.

7. *MADONNA AND CHILD WITH SAINTS IGNATIUS OF LOYOLA, FRANCIS XAVIER, COSMAS AND DAMIAN*. Oil on canvas. 24 x 15¾ inches (60 x 40 cm). A radiograph shows minor *pentimenti* around the head and right hand of the Virgin, whose blue mantle may have been retouched. COLLECTIONS: An inscription on the back reads: *Cet original de Carlo Maratta a été legue par Marechal* (next two lines canceled and illegible even with infra-red light) *1770*. Presumably therefore in the collection of a French Marshal in 1770. The present owner found the picture in Ireland. LITERATURE: A. Sutherland Harris, *Andrea Sacchi*, unpublished dissertation, University of London, 1964, pp. 65–66.

A slightly larger version of this sketch is known, coming from the Barberini collection, now belonging to Professor Roberto Longhi in Florence (*L'ideale classico del seicento*, Bologna, 1962, p. 339, pl. 139 *bis*). The composition of both sketches is almost identical with the ceiling fresco in the Old Pharmacy of the Collegio Romano in Rome. The room also contains ten frescoed lunettes depicting ten pioneers of the art of medicine; an inscription next to Galen gives the finishing date, May of 1629, and names the two artists responsible, Sacchi and Emilio

Savonanzi, the latter a minor Bolognese painter to whom the ten lunettes can be ascribed. The site explains the presence in Sacchi's composition of the two Jesuit saints, Francis Xavier and Ignatius of Loyola, and of the two patron saints of medicine, Cosmas and Damian. No coats-of-arms or symbols of the Barberini appear in the room, but the fact that they at one time owned both a preparatory oil sketch and a larger version of the ceiling fresco (H. Posse, *Der römische Maler Andrea Sacchi,* Leipzig, 1925, p. 110) suggests that they were involved in some way.

Since the composition is identical in both sketches, it seems unlikely that both were made during preparation of the final design. The sketch made for that purpose must therefore have been copied by the artist himself, either as a record after the work was completed, when the original sketch was perhaps given to the patron, or for another patron who expressed interest in the work. Very possibly the latter hypothesis is the correct one. In March, 1631, a diamond merchant called Valguarnera is known to have had in his possession a small picture (*quadretto*) by Sacchi, the subject of which was "St. Ignatius with the Madonna and other Saints," which he had bought from Sacchi for 30 scudi (J. Costello, "The Twelve Pictures 'ordered by Velazquez' and the Trial of Valguarnera," *Journal of the Warburg and Courtauld Institutes,* XIII, 1950, pp. 271, 273). Valguarnera's picture was most probably a version of the Collegio Romano fresco because Sacchi is not known to have painted St. Ignatius on any other occasion. Also several of Valguarnera's other purchases at this time were copies of existing works made after the originals, either by the artists themselves or by assistants. The difference in the present condition of the two sketches is worth noting here. Professor Longhi's is darker than Mr. Sewell's, suggesting that both the priming layer and upper paint layers of the former are thinner, and consequently that it was the more rapidly painted of the two. Professor Longhi's version might therefore be the earlier sketch, made in 1629, while Mr. Sewell's, a more carefully prepared work, was perhaps painted in 1630 for Valguarnera. Alternatively, Valguarnera may simply have bought the version which Sacchi had painted for himself.

Apart from the difference in color noted above, and the slight difference in size, the two sketches are identical. Both show more sky and more putti on the left side and less sky below than does the fresco. Like most of Sacchi's other surviving sketches, they concentrate on the figures and not on the whole composition. A preparatory drawing for the figure of St. Ignatius at Windsor (A. F. Blunt and H. L. Cooke, *Roman Drawings . . . at Windsor Castle,* London, 1960, No. 202 verso: catalogued as by Lanfranco) also attests to the care with which Sacchi prepared this work.   A.S.H.

Lent by Mr. Brian Sewell, London

PIER FRANCESCO MOLA (1612–1666)

Mola began his career in Rome in the studios of Prospero Orsi and the Cavaliere d'Arpino. From 1633 onwards he spent 14 years in travel, working all the time and studying North Italian artists: Albani and Guercino in Bologna, Titian, Veronese and the Bassano family in Venice. In Rome from 1647 until his death, Mola often worked with the Cortona circle. He shared in painting such fresco decorations as those in the Quirinal and the Gesù, but his quality is seen at its best in smaller oil paintings with landscapes. Along with Testa and Rosa, Mola moved away from the ideal landscape of Poussin to a more personal and romantic form.

8. *CARTHUSIANS IN A LANDSCAPE.* Oil on canvas. Inscribed on the back: *del Mola.* 13¾ x 18 inches (35 x 46 cm).

9. *FRANCISCANS IN A LANDSCAPE.* Oil on canvas. Inscribed on the back: *del Mola.* 14¼ x 18 inches (36 x 46 cm). EXHIBITION: *Il seicento europeo,* Rome, 1956-57, Nos. 213, 214.

These landscape sketches show the style of Mola at its freshest. Quickly set down by a rapid brush that defines forms, light, and space at once, the sketches show Mola's ultimate debt to Venetian painting, equally revealed by the rich palette and warm tones. The atmosphere of excitement gives a romantic quality to the sketches, perhaps surprising to modern eyes, but one may emphasize that they are not studies from nature: the bridge-like rock in the *Carthusians* and the balanced asymmetry in the *Franciscans* are the results of a disciplined structure. The palm trees add an exotic note, suggesting far-away lands, and they point to what may have been the purpose of the sketches, namely to prepare a series of hermit saints. Mola also did drawings of landscapes with monks or other figures (A. Blunt and H. L. Cooke, *The Roman Drawings . . . at Windsor Castle,* 1960, Nos. 542–6), and one of his best known pictures, *St. Bruno in Ecstasy,* depends on the landscape to give drama and expression to the figure. The *St. Bruno,* known in several versions (*Seicento,* No. 210), dates late in Mola's career, perhaps *circa* 1665. We cannot be precise in dating our sketches, but they were surely done after Mola's return to Rome, and a cautious dating to *circa* 1650 is at the moment the best that can be offered.   M.L.G.

Lent by N. U. l'Architetto Andrea Busiri Vici, Rome

SALVATOR ROSA (1615–1673)

Rosa spent his youth in Naples, where he studied with his uncle Domenico Antonio Greco and worked in the shop of Ribera and of Falcone. Rosa then moved to Rome and worked there until his death except for the years 1641–49, spent in Florence. Famous for his landscapes and scenes in landscape settings, Rosa preferred to be known as a history painter in the grand manner. A writer and musician as well as a painter and etcher, Rosa composed many poems and satires on the Florentine and Roman life of his time.

10. *PINDAR AND PAN.* Oil on canvas. 39⅛ x 29 inches (99.7 x 74 cm). EXHIBITION: Koetser Gallery, London, 1966. LITERATURE: B. Nicolson, "Current . . . Exhibitions," *Burlington Magazine,* CVIII, 1966, p. 211, Fig. 55; Rosa letters in U. Limentani, ed., *Poesie e lettere inedite di Salvator Rosa* (Biblioteca dell' "Archivium Romanicum," ser. 1, XXXI), Florence, 1950, Nos. XXXIX, XL.

Rosa oil sketches are uncommon. This one is a preparation for the very large painting of *Pindar and Pan,* formerly in the Chigi Collection in Rome (L. Salerno, *Rosa,* Milan, 1963, No. 87). Rosa himself discusses the picture in a letter, noting that it was sent along with two others to a public exhibition held at the Roman church of S. Giovanni Decollato in August, 1666. The sketch is not mentioned, but there is no doubt that it belongs to a late phase in the design of the ex-Chigi painting. Pan appears in the pose of the bozzetto, but Rosa gave him more hair and a set of pipes in the final version. Pindar, however, is altered. In the sketch he is a vital figure who sits on the ground and engages actively in dialogue with the god of Arcady. In the finished picture he is presented more officially with laurel wreath and cloak and is re-interpreted as a passive figure, sitting on a rock and gesturing inwards. The changes clarify the iconography but weaken the expressive power found in the sketch, painted in short firm strokes in rich warm tones. Yet these changes were clearly deliberate: in the final painting Pindar's face looks oddly weak and bewildered, but Rosa implied in a second letter that he gave Pindar a spiritual air rather than a beautiful face to emphasize that Pan loved Pindar more for his poetry than his beauty.

The subject, according to Rosa himself, is unique: in a wood the God Pan is seen in discourse with Pindar, taking pleasure in his poetry (Letter XXXIX). The theme, involving the spiritual elevation of those whom the gods love, comes from one of Rosa's favorite Roman authors, Plutarch, in this case from the life of Numa where Plutarch says that Pan loved Pindar and his poetry. It is characteristic of Rosa's temperament that such a learned theme should fire his imagination; and he took equal pride in the erudition of the subjects of the other two pictures that he had also sent along to the exhibition of 1666: *Aethra Showing Theseus Where His Father Aegeus Had Hidden His Shoes and Sword* (from Plutarch) and *The Centaur Chiron Teaching Music, Medicine, and Astrology to the Young Achilles* (from Ovid's *Fasti*). Rosa also thought that the quality of painting of these three was "the best that I have done till now," but in the case of the *Pindar and Pan*, his satisfaction was mistaken. The sketch on view has a strength and vigor entirely lacking in the rhetoric of the final picture and its life-size figures.   C.L. and M.L.G.

Lent by Mr. and Mrs. Milton J. Lewine, New York

FILIPPO LAURI (1623–1694)

Born in Rome where he lived all his life, Lauri was the son of an Antwerp landscape painter, Balthasar Lauwers, who had been an assistant of Paul Brill. Lauri studied first with his father, and his attention to detail and to genre motifs reflects this Flemish background. He worked under the Caravaggist Caroselli and was elected to the Academy of St. Luke in 1654. He also had his own academy, a meeting-place for patrons and intellectuals. He was a master of small landscapes set with mythological or religious subjects, but he also worked under Cortona, in particular in the frescoed gallery of the Quirinal palace, in 1656–1657.

11. *WALL DECORATIONS WITH AUTUMN AND WINTER.* Oil on canvas. 15 x 25¾ inches (38.1 x 65.4 cm). COLLECTION: Busiri Vici, Rome. EXHIBITION: *Seventeenth and Eighteenth Century Italian Paintings,* Hazlitt Gallery, London, 1963, No. 14. LITERATURE: B. Riccio, "Vita di Filippo Lauri di Francesco Saverio Baldinucci," *Commentari,* X, 1959, pp. 9–10. (Brief notices: B. Nicolson, *Burlington Magazine,* CV, 1963, p. 227; T. Crombie, *Apollo,* LXXVII, 1963, pp. 405–406.)

As recognized by Riccio, this charming sketch represents a preparatory stage in the decoration of the great gallery of the Villa Farnese on the Palatine, demolished in the last century. According to the younger Baldinucci (Riccio, p. 10), Cardinal Girolamo Farnese assigned the decorations of the four seasons in the gallery to Carlo Cignani. Cignani had barely finished the *Summer* when the cardinal, probably *circa* 1662, transferred the work to Lauri, who finished the gallery, adding figures, celestial signs and planets, festoons, and statues in chiaroscuro, all in a painted architectural setting. Our sketch is a unique and precious record of the work, although other material that may be connected with the decorations has come down to us: four paintings of the seasons, engraved by Vitalba and Ravenet in 1770 when they were in the collection of the Duke of Devonshire at Chatsworth, four small modelli for these (Busiri Vici Collection, Rome), and still another related pair (Private Collection, London).

In this bozzetto Lauri has approached the problem of adjusting the scenes, decorative figures, and *trompe-l'œil* architecture to that complex part of the room where the vaulted ceiling meets the wall. Accepting this structure, Lauri accentuates it with painted moldings and architectural members, creating the illusion of actual supports for figures and actual frames for the pictures of the seasons. The one inset scene we see was called *Spring* by Riccio, but it is surely *Autumn* (Nicolson, p. 227) since it shows a Bacchanalian revel with grapes and wine, while the decorative head above carries a basket of fruit and flowers which refers to the harvest. Yet the identification as *Spring* is understandable, for the flowers and the nudity of the small bright figures suggest a cheerful, pleasant, springtime scene. Such formal and thematic ease gives a pre-Rococo flavor to Lauri's work, but the firmness of the colors and solidity of the architecture belong strictly to the Roman Baroque.

The same light ease is seen in the other figures. The inset panel at the right is blank, but the shivering putti who warm their hands at the fire tell us that the subject was to be *Winter*. And between the scenes sits Mercury, belonging to Lauri's scheme of heavenly signs and planets, traditional and fitting for a ceiling.   M.L.G.

Lent by Mrs. Jacqueline Humphris, London

Attributed to GIOVANNI PAOLO SCHOR (1615–1674)

Johann Paul Schor, in Italy usually called Giovanni Paolo Tedesco, was born in Innsbruck into a family of versatile artists. In Rome by 1640, he became a member of the Academy of St. Luke in 1654. Schor's work as a painter shows him in the Cortona succession. In the late 1650's and the 1660's he worked extensively for Bernini, who held him in high esteem. He was much in demand for designs for stuccoes, and decorations of almost every kind of object—stage scenery, tapestries, fountains, coaches, candelabra and vases—were within his reach. He died in Rome.

12. *MERMAIDS AND CUPIDS.* Oil on canvas. 15¼ x 20¼ inches (38.7 x 51.3 cm). Slight damage in lower left corner; large crack along bottom. COLLECTION: Hearth.

This bozzetto, hitherto unpublished, has been attributed to the Venetian School (*ca.* 1750) as well as to the circle of Pietro da Cortona. The latter attribution is certainly close to the truth, as is shown by both the pale green voluminous female 'tritons' balancing flower baskets on their heads and the playful 'Raphaelesque' putti. A careful examination of this engaging decorative piece makes it possible to claim Schor's authorship, for many striking similarities with his known work can be established. A Schor drawing at Windsor (A. Blunt and H. L. Cooke, *The Roman Drawings . . . at Windsor Castle,* London, 1960, pl. 46) with figural decorations for a coach contains two putti flying about a cornucopia who are so close to the pair on the top left of our sketch that they may almost be called a signature. Moreover, one discovers common idiosyncrasies such as the putti with pudgy legs that have no ankles. Comparisons may also be made with the female sea denizens in Schor's Cortonesque decoration of the great gallery in the Palazzo Colonna, 1665–8, or with the atlantes with wicker baskets of fruit and flowers on their heads that decorate a fountain made on Schor's design in the garden of the Palazzo Borghese (before 1672; H. Hibbard, *Burlington Magazine,* C, 1958, pp. 205 ff).

If all this material, in addition to much more that must be left unmentioned, helps to support the attribution to Schor, the precise purpose of the bozzetto remains an enigma. It may have been done in preparation for the decoration of a room which may well survive in Rome. The style of the sketch would indicate a date in the 1670's.

M.L.G.

Lent by the Cooper Union Museum, New York

GIOVANNI BATTISTA GAULLI called BACICCIO (1639–1709)

Gaulli came to Rome sometime after the Genoese plague of 1657 and worked there for the rest of his life. His style was first formed in Genoa on Rubens, van Dyck and Strozzi and later in Rome on Bernini; in 1669 he went to Modena and Parma where he studied Correggio. In Rome he made his name as a portrait and fresco painter in the grand manner. His most important and most extensive fresco cycle is the decoration of the Gesù, executed under Bernini's influence between 1672 and 1685. After 1685 his exuberant style tuned down and his palette became paler. He made a number of bozzetti, which display a light touch, free handling of paint, and luminous color.

13. *THE FOUR DOCTORS OF THE LATIN CHURCH.* Oil on canvas. 29 x 26½ inches (75 x 66 cm). EXHIBITION: IBM Gallery, New York, 1963; *An Exhibition of Paintings, Bozzetti and Drawings by Baciccio,* Allen Memorial Art Museum, Oberlin College, 1967, No. 8. LITERATURE: R. Enggass, *The Paintings of Baciccio,* Pennsylvania State University Press, 1964, pp. 40, 134; Museo de Arte de Ponce, *Catalogue,* Ponce, 1965, I, pp. 70–71; *Allen Memorial Art Museum Bulletin,* XXIV, 1967 (exhibition catalogue), No. 8.

This sketch is one of two extant oil studies for one of the pendentives of the dome of the Gesù in Rome. In the other three pendentives are the four Evangelists, four Old Testament Prophets, and four Old Testament Lawgivers and Leaders. These sixteen figures make a symbolic transition between the congregation below—the mass of the faithful— and the vision of Heaven displayed in the dome above.

An oil sketch in Naples (Enggass, fig. 61) shows an earlier and freer version of our pendentive. The Ponce sketch is closer to the execution and *pentimenti* indicate the development of Gaulli's thought as he worked with the brush: he moved the head of St. Augustine, first placed next to St. Jerome, closer to St. Gregory, thus preparing the final asymmetrical composition. The changes in the finished work are mainly iconographic: St. Augustine's angel now holds a flaming heart, St. Jerome's angel now points to the cardinal's hat, the saint's traditional attribute, and Jerome himself holds a rock, symbol of mortification. Such changes, probably due to instructions of the Jesuits, help to clarify the meaning of the figures and to enhance the expressive intensity in the group. But the densely constructed composition and the rhythmic flow of forms had been basically solved in the Ponce sketch.

Drawings and bozzetti for other pendentives show early stages in the development of Gaulli's thought (Enggass, figs. 58, 59, 98, 99). They give an idea of the care with which he prepared these frescoes and allow the conclusion that even the Naples bozzetto was preceded by earlier preparatory studies on paper as well as on canvas.

Our bozzetto, dating from 1675–76, reveals Gaulli's early mature style under the influence of Bernini. With its swelling forms and massive drapery that seem to translate sculpture into paint, the sketch is a splendid example of Gaulli's High Baroque manner in Rome. And since the Naples bozzetto has been changed into a 'finished' picture by the subsequent addition of architecture and a landscape, our sketch here gives a clearer picture of Gaulli's oil preparation.   P.M.E.

Lent by the Ponce Museum of Art, Puerto Rico (The Luis A. Ferré Foundation)

ANDREA POZZO (1642–1709)

Andrea Pozzo, the last great practitioner and theorist of Baroque *quadratura* painting, was born in 1642 at Trent. He became a Jesuit lay brother at the age of 23. His career was spent in the north of Italy until 1681, when he was called to Rome by the Jesuit General Padre Oliva, on the advice of Carlo Maratti. Pozzo remained active in Rome until 1702 when he left for Vienna, where he worked until his death in 1709. Perhaps more appreciated there than in Rome, his work had great influence on the development of German and Austrian fresco painting.

14. *ALLEGORY OF THE MISSIONARY WORK OF THE JESUITS.* Oil on canvas. 69½ x 135¼ inches (178 x 346 cm). COLLECTION: Collegio Romano until 1895. EXHIBITION: *Il seicento europeo,* Rome, 1956, No. 231. LITERATURE: H. Voss, *Die Malerei des Barock in Rom,* Berlin, 1924, p. 583; E. K. Waterhouse, *Baroque Painting in Rome,* London, 1937, p. 87. For Pozzo's ceiling, see also E. Feinblatt, "Jesuit Ceiling Decoration," *Art Quarterly,* X, 1947, pp. 246–53.

This painting is the model for Pozzo's enormous ceiling fresco of S. Ignazio, which is perhaps the most grandiloquent visual manifestation of the triumphant spirit of the Catholic Restoration. The ceiling celebrates the work of the Jesuits in all the corners of the world. Pozzo explained the iconography, in a letter of 1694 to the Prince of Liechtenstein, as a visualization of an injunction of St. Ignatius, "Go and light a flame over the world," based on a verse in St. Luke (XII: 49). Above a vast illusionistic architecture that extends the real church into heaven, St. Ignatius kneels on a cloud before Christ, the precise spiritual and actual center of the composition. From the saint's heart beams of light pour out, illuminating representations of the four continents— Africa, America, Asia, and Europe—while a heavenly host rejoices in the act.

The ceiling was commissioned in 1691 and completed in 1694. Pascoli tells us that Pozzo first worked out the design in ink and then on a larger scale in color (*Vite,* 1730–36, II, p. 258). The latter is surely identifiable with the sketch shown here, for this was the modello exhibited in the Collegio Romano to test public reaction. Pascoli noted that almost everyone who inspected the modello liked the concept, but, he continued (perhaps not without a touch of irony framed as a compliment), it was unanimously felt that because of the overpowering complexity of the composition Pozzo, when painting the work, must have thought "not of the brevity of our lives, but of infinitude and eternity."

At the time of painting, Pozzo's illusionist architecture (*quadratura*) was old-fashioned in Rome. Yet his solution, in part owing to the immensity of the scale, is an epitome of Baroque painting, and generations have stood amazed at his virtuosity.   D.M.

Lent by the Galleria Nazionale d'Arte Antica in Palazzo Corsini, Rome

GIOVANNI PAOLO PANINI (1691–1765)

Panini was first trained in his native Piacenza, learning from Bibiena and other masters of scenographic art. In 1711 he moved to Rome, where he joined the studio of Luti and established his reputation with the fresco decorations, now destroyed, of the Villa Patrizi of 1718–1725. His close connection with the French circle in Rome gained him many commissions. Like Gaspar van Wittel, called Vanvitelli (1653–1736), Panini did descriptive topographical views of Rome, but he is closer to the more romantic tradition of Giovanni Ghisolfi (1623–1683), and his *capricci,* fantasy views of the antique monuments, had an enormous vogue both at home and abroad.

15. *SKETCH FOR THE FÊTE IN THE PIAZZA NAVONA, ROME, ON THE BIRTH OF THE DAUPHIN OF FRANCE, 1729.* Oil on canvas. 10⅝ x 18 inches (27 x 45.8 cm). COLLECTION: F. Kleinberger and Co., Inc. EXHIBITIONS: *Italian Baroque Painting and Drawing,* F. Kleinberger Galleries, New York, 1932? (listed among paintings of the second half of the 17th century); *Italian Baroque Painting,* Palace of the Legion of Honor, San Francisco, 1941, No. 82. LITERATURE: H. de Chennevières, "Jean-Paul Panini, peintre de fêtes publiques," *L'Art,* XXI, 1880, pp. 97–105, 121–126; S. Rocheblave, *Charles-Nicolas Cochin,* Paris, 1927, p. 11; H. Tietze, *Masterpieces of European Painting in America,* London, 1939, pl. 117; F. Arisi, *Gian Paolo Panini,* Piacenza (Casa di Risparmio), 1961, p. 138, fig. 127; *Paintings in the Art Institute of Chicago,* Chicago, 1961, p. 349.

As an artist trained in scenography—he was indeed Professor of Perspective at the French Academy in Rome—Panini preferred to do preparatory work in drawings. His oil bozzetti are very few in number, and this sketch may be considered chronologically the first among those that have come down to us (Arisi, p. 138). The dating is of course simple and precise. Cardinal de Polignac, the French Ambassador to the Holy See, gave a great public *festa* in the Piazza Navona on November 30, 1729, to celebrate the birth of the Dauphin of France. He commissioned Panini to design the decorations and record the event; the Cardinal presented the first version, dated 1729, to Louis XV and the picture is now in the Louvre. Panini obviously worked rapidly to record the decorations before they were dismantled and painted the final picture at once. Later he made a second version, now in Dublin (National Gallery of Ireland, No. 95), signed and dated 1731 (Pl. 15A).

Our sketch is a preparation for a surprisingly small part of the finished picture, a detail in the lower left-hand corner showing the last-minute decorations about to be set up while ladies and gentlemen look around in conversation. In the final versions the figures have been shifted about: the two ladies and the gentleman in the upper left have been placed farther to the left, and the whole group to the right of the pole was re-located, with changes, farther to the right. In the new space thus created Panini inserted two workers setting up poles, matched on the right by other workmen. This last observation may supply the clue to the changes, for central in the sketch is a workman carrying a coat-of-arms. But in the final composition, extremely symmetrical for all its air of easy movement, this honored position would have been lost and so Panini shifted the workman with the coat-of-arms to the central group.

The colorful sketch shows Panini's gifts to great advantage. With a full brush he jots down lights and colors at once, never losing a sense of specific detail or of revealing pose and gesture. His feeling for structure informs the sketch, making a satisfactory composition out of what was intended to be only a detail, and his figures glow with life and movement. The whole is bathed in the sparkle of a brilliant sun, a glitter appropriate for the happy event, although rare for a November day in Rome.   D.W.P.

Lent by The Art Institute of Chicago, Simeon B. Williams Fund

FRANCESCO MANCINI (1679–1758)

Around 1710, Mancini was a student of the Bolognese Carlo Cignani, but he rapidly assumed Maratti's style after he arrived in Rome *circa* 1724, at which time he was elected a member of the Academy of St. Luke. He received many commissions in Rome, yet in about 1737 he returned to his birthplace, S. Angelo in Vado

(Romagna), where he executed most of his mature work. He also worked in the Marches and in Umbria. Later still he returned to Rome and for two consecutive years, 1750–1751, was elected President of the Academy of St. Luke, remaining active in Rome until his death.

16. *ST. PHILIP NERI IN ECSTASY.* Oil on canvas. 38½ x 26 inches (98.5 x 67.2 cm). COLLECTION: Tartaglia, Rome. EXHIBITION: *Pittura italiana del seicento e del settecento,* Florence, 1922, No. 869 (as Andrea Sacchi). LITERATURE: H. Voss, *Die Malerei des Barock in Rom,* Berlin, 1924, p. 612 and pl. 370; M. Nugent, *Alla mostra della pittura italiana del seicento e del settecento,* Florence, 1930, II, pp. 390–2 (as Andrea Sacchi).

This sketch represents a standard scene from the life of St. Philip Neri in which the Virgin and Child, surrounded by angels, appear to him during an illness. The subject was popular in Rome and elsewhere and was painted by Reni, Franceschini, and Maratti, all of whose pictures Mancini may have seen. As Voss recognized, the sketch is a preparation for the altarpiece of the church of S. Filippo Neri in Macerata. Voss dated it in the 1730's, but it may be much earlier, since Voss did not then know the exact date of Mancini's birth, now documented (N. Ridarelli, *Rassegna Marchigiana,* VIII, 1924, p. 324).

The gray tone of the sketch is typical of Mancini, who preferred delicate colors worked in smoky shades. Here his loose handling of the brush creates an active linear movement across the surface, endowing the scene with a ghostly and visionary quality by the play of strokes that are almost independent of the figures themselves. Details are cursory, and Mancini is more interested in the light falling on the forms than in their modeling. The style is peculiarly fitting for the subject, showing both saint and apparition as a mystical and ephemeral dream.

J.K.

Lent by the Galleria Nazionale d'Arte Antica in Palazzo Corsini, Rome

PIERRE SUBLEYRAS (1699–1749)

Born in Saint-Gilles-du-Gard (Languedoc), Subleyras was trained first in the provinces with his father Mathieu and other masters, and then in Paris at the Ecole de l'Académie Royale. He won the *Prix de Rome* in 1727; in the following year he took up residence at the Villa Medici in Rome and managed to extend his stay for seven years. But though he left the Academy in 1735, he established his permanent home in Rome, where his luminous palette and reflective compositions earned him wide popularity.

17. *ST. BENEDICT REVIVING A CHILD.* Oil on canvas. 16¼ x 10¾ inches (41.5 x 27.5 cm). EXHIBITIONS: *Museum Masterpieces,* Mobile Art Gallery, Alabama, 1964, No. 19; *La peinture française: collections américaines,* Bordeaux, 1966, No. 30, pl. 12. LITERATURE: A. P. F. Robert-Dumesnil, *Le peintre-graveur français,* II, 1836, No. 4 (as St. Bruno) ; *Art Quarterly,* XXV, 1962, p. 268; W. H. Ackland Memorial Art Center, *An Introduction to the Collection, 1958–1962,* Chapel Hill, 1963, No. 12, pl. 12; *Apollo,* LXXVIII, 1963, p. 71, fig. 3.

This oil sketch was executed in preparation for one of two altarpieces commissioned by the Olivetans of Perugia, *St. Benedict Reviving a Child,* painted in 1744, and *St. Ambrose Absolving Theodosius,* painted in 1745. The subject of the *St. Benedict* picture is found in the *Dialogues of St. Gregory,* Book II, chapter xxxii. A gardener came to the monastery with his dead child and begged St. Benedict to resuscitate him. The saint lay down on the body of the child, like Elijah and Elisha, and breathed life into him again. The layman in the left foreground, more actively concerned with the event than his counterpart at the right, is surely the child's father. The other figure, not mentioned in the *Dialogues,* must be regarded as one of those genre elements that Subleyras characteristically included in his works. St. Benedict is dressed in white instead of the usual black, relating him to the white Olivetan monks, reform Benedictines, who stand behind the saint and contemplate the miracle.

Subleyras prepared the composition of the *St. Benedict* with immense care, and at least three other sketches and two drawings, sometimes with the saint incorrectly identified, have come down to us (O. Arnaud, "Subleyras," in L. Dimier, *Les peintres français du XVIIIe siécle,* Paris, 1930, II, p. 77, Nos. 52–54 and p. 86, No. 31; and L. Lagrange in *Gazette des Beaux-Arts,* V, 1860, p. 141).

The sketch exhibited here shows a subtlety and variety in the handling of the whites of the monks' robes that remain the key coloristic device in the final altarpiece. The concern with the luminosity of ascetic whites is found throughout Subleyras' entire career and is typical for the artist's works. These whites frequently are seen to best advantage in the sketches rather than in the finished pictures.

The altarpiece of *St. Benedict* is also known in an etching by Lerouge and Mignet. The picture remained in Perugia until 1822 when it was moved to its present location, the church of S. Francesca Romana in Rome. The companion picture remains in Perugia.   M.C.A.

Lent by the Ackland Art Center, University of North Carolina, Chapel Hill, North Carolina

POMPEO BATONI (1708–1787)

Born in Lucca, Batoni went to Rome in 1728 where he studied Raphael and the antique as much as the work of his teachers, Conca, Masucci, and Imperiali. He began his career painting miniatures and copies, but he soon gained commissions for important religious works and in 1741 he became a member of the Academy of St. Luke. Although his works ranged widely over all subjects, he became internationally famous for his portraits. Batoni was receptive to the rising Neo-classicism and was a friend of A. R. Mengs. Their styles differed, however, and Batoni's eulogist, Boni, stated: "Batoni was more a painter than philosopher, Mengs more a philosopher than painter."

18. *ALLEGORY OF THE ARTS*. Oil on canvas. 11⅝ x 8⅞ inches (29.5 x 22.5 cm). COLLECTION: Count Merenda. LITERATURE: L. Marcucci, "Pompeo Batoni a Forlì," *Emporium*, XCIX, 1944, pp. 101–102; A. M. Clark, "Some Early Subject Pictures by P. E. Batoni," *Burlington Magazine*, CI, 1959, pp. 235, 237. (For the final picture, see Städelsches Kunstinstitut, *Verzeichnis der Gemälde*, Frankfurt, 1924, No. 731; E. Emmerling, *Pompeo Batoni*, Darmstadt, 1932, No. 169.)

This sketch is precisely dated from the signature on the large painting now in Frankfurt: *Pompejus Battonius Lucensis, pinxit, An. D. MDCCXL*. The sketch thus belongs to Batoni's early maturity and shows his desire for a clear and rational composition handled in warm and delicate colors. Batoni's ease in placing his figures in such a spacious setting obscures the fact that the grouping is novel. Earlier pictures do, of course, show various figures of the arts together, but Batoni's is the first to combine all five in the same setting. Painting sits at the easel portraying Mercury, god of eloquence and inventor of the lyre, and turns to Poetry, who wears a laurel wreath and carries a lyre; at her feet are books, which in the final picture have the names of Homer and Virgil on their spines. At the feet of these ladies sits Sculpture, while Music, with a double flute, looks over Poetry's shoulder. Above them all sits Architecture, seemingly lost in thought. Whatever private significance the subject may have had for Batoni, the prominence given Poetry and Painting, shown in serious dialogue, is a visual affirmation of Batoni's belief in the old, classic tradition: "As in poetry, so in painting." But Batoni's sketch also shows that he did not allow himself to be overwhelmed by the rising tide of Neo-classicism. The elegance of the ladies, the coloring, and the firm composition link him to the Late Baroque in Rome.   M.C.A.

Lent by N. U. l'Architetto Andrea Busiri Vici, Rome

GIUSEPPE CADES (1750–1799)

Cades was a pupil of Corvi in Rome, where he was born and worked throughout his life. An extremely facile painter, draughtsman, and engraver, Cades was able to imitate and even counterfeit the work of such older artists as Raphael and Michelangelo. He entered the Academy of St. Luke in 1786 and executed decorative works for such patrons as the Chigi, the Borghese and Catherine the Great, works that display his love of pageantry. A rich palette and bravura brush-stroke mark his eclectic style, and his pageant scenes anticipate Romantic history painting of the next century.

19. *THE STORY OF COUNT GAUTIER.* Oil on canvas mounted on panel. 4½ x 9¼ inches (11.5 x 23.5 cm). EXHIBITION: *Il settecento a Roma,* Rome, 1959, No. 112. LITERATURE: None. (For the artist and the final fresco, see H. Voss, *Die Malerei des Barock in Rom,* Berlin, 1924, pp. 665–666 and pl. 432.)

This is a sketch for a ceiling fresco in the Villa Borghese in Rome, commissioned in 1787. The story comes from Boccaccio's *Decameron.* When the King of France and his son went off to war, they left Gautier, Count of Antwerp, as regent; the princess, daughter-in-law of the King, fell in love with him. Like Potiphar's wife and Joseph, she made her proposal, Gautier rejected her, and she cried out that she was being attacked. Leaving all his possessions behind, Gautier fled to London, left his son and daughter Violante with people who would raise them, and went off to Ireland. Many years later, still poor, he returned to find his children rich and happy. Cades, adapting the story slightly, shows the moment when the poor count, disguised as a beggar, comes to his daughter's house in London. He is not recognized by her nor, of course, by her husband, but their children are somehow instinctively drawn to the old man, their unknown grandfather.

With complete control of color and chiaroscuro, Cades quickly jotted down the composition in the sketch before us. He has already decided to set the scene outdoors, departing from Boccaccio, and contrasts the stable group of Violante and her husband with the active group of Gautier and the children. At the same time an adumbrated architecture suggests the locale, while the strokes of light and color prepare the way for textures and costumes. This first idea for the fresco contains all the basic forms of the picture, but Cades developed his ideas in still another sketch (New York) and in a more finished bozzetto, a true modello, now in the Art Institute of Chicago (Pl. 19A): in the latter he lowered the viewpoint, connected the two groups by shifting the horseman from the left to the center, and strengthened Gautier's figure. He was also concerned with costume and setting, further animating and detailing the dress and changing the buildings to a Gothic tower on the left and a Gothic church behind the children. In the fresco (Pl. 19B) he returned to the stepped platform of the first sketch but followed in general what we see in the second. The most revealing change concerns the architecture: the church is now reminiscent of Venetian Gothic buildings while the London palace of Violante and her husband closely follows the design of the Doge's palace in Venice.

This strange admixture is a key to Cades' romantic approach. Rejecting the notion of historic verisimilitude, so dear to Neo-classic painters and theorists, Cades preferred instead picturesque references to a medieval past. A 14th-century story set in a London of Venetian Gothic with figures wearing costumes that would be more at home in a work by Rubens points to a distinctly proto-Romantic state of mind, imaginative rather than archaeological in presenting a historical narrative.   P.M.E.

Lent by Mr. Brinsley Ford, London

NAPLES

BERNARDO CAVALLINO (1616–1656)

Cavallino presents a very personal note in Neapolitan painting of his time, with delicate representations of graceful figures. His dusky pictures with luminous accents reveal his debt to Caravaggio, whose style he learned through the softened versions of Stanzione and Artemisia Gentileschi in Naples. He also derived ideas from Flemish painting and its variants in Genoa and Rome, revealed in the small size and glowing tonality of his works and in their close observation of nature. He received few public commissions, and little is known about his life.

20. *ST. CECILIA.* Oil on canvas. 24 x 19½ inches (62 x 49 cm). COLLECTION: Domenico Barbaia. EXHIBITIONS: *Mostra della pittura italiana del seicento e del settecento,* Palazzo Pitti, Florence, 1922, No. 251; *Exposition de l'art italien,* Petit Palais, Paris, 1935, No. 101; *La mostra della pittura napolitana dei secoli XVII, XVIII e XIX,* Naples, 1938, p. 65; *Masterworks of Five Centuries,* Golden Gate International Exhibition, San Francisco, 1939; *Italian Masters lent by the Royal Italian Government,* Museum of Modern Art, New York, 1940, No. 25. LITERATURE: A. de Rinaldis, *Pinacoteca del Museo Nazionale di Napoli,* 1911, pp. 415–16; A. de Rinaldis, *Bernardo Cavallino,* Rome, 1921, pl. XII; E. Sestieri, "Ricerche su Cavallino," *Dedalo,* II, 1921, p. 193; M. Nugent, *Alla mostra della pittura italiana del seicento e del settecento,* Florence, 1930, II, pp. 575–577; A. de Rinaldis, "Le Caravage et l'évolution de la peinture napolitaine au XVIIe siecle," *Formes,* XXX, 1932, pp. 324–326; B. Molajoli, *Il Museo di Capodimonte,* Naples, 1961, pl. L; A. Percy, *Bernardo Cavallino,* unpublished M.A. Thesis, Pennsylvania State University, 1965, p. 52 (complete bibliography).

St. Cecilia, the patron saint of music and musicians, is shown in a moment of religious ecstasy. With head raised and eyes toward heaven, she swoons onto her knees, leaving her instrument on a palm frond, symbol of martyrdom; an angel acknowledges her sanctity, holding a flowered wreath over her head.

This is a sketch for the large oil painting of 1645, Cavallino's only dated work. It was commissioned for the church of S. Antoniello delle Monache in Naples—where this sketch was also hung—but is now in the Palazzo Vecchio in Florence (illustrated in *Mostra della pittura italiana. . . ,* 1922, p. 62). Another oil sketch for the picture, of nearly the same size but with smaller figures, was in the Santangelo collection in Naples in the 19th century but has since disappeared.

This image of St. Cecilia is typical of Cavallino's work in its small size and graceful figures and poses. Also characteristic is his use of a selective lighting of forms seen against a reddish brown ground, a method that ultimately derives from Caravaggio. Cavallino was famous for his harmonious coloring, and we can appreciate this here in the melodious blues, dark golds, and tones of gray and dark green united by the pervading, warm red-brown ground. The delicate brush lines of thick paint used to outline the folds and shadows of the drapery are additional characteristics of his work. The type of the saint's head, raised, shown in a three-quarters profile, and modeled by strong contrasts of light and dark, is quite similar to those of Vaccaro, a slightly older contemporary, with whose work Cavallino's paintings have often been confused. But Cavallino's emotional expression, quietly serious and sensitive in interpretation, make him a distinctive figure in Neapolitan painting of his time.   J.K.

Lent by the Museo e Gallerie Nazionali di Capodimonte, Naples

MATTIA PRETI (1613–1699)

Preti, known as "Il Cavalier Calabrese" because he was born in Calabria, was intermittently in Rome between 1630 and 1661, during which time he also worked in Modena and Venice. The strongest impression on him was made by Caravaggio, and he combined his Caravaggism with the other lessons learned in Rome and North Italy to create his own powerful High Baroque style, a style he introduced to Naples during the years 1656–1660. His best works are in Naples, where he became a strong influence on such younger artists as Solimena. Except for brief trips to Naples for special commissions, he spent the years from 1661 until his death in Malta.

21. *THE MARTYRDOM OF ST. CATHERINE.* Oil on canvas. 40 x 29 9/16 inches (102 x 75.5 cm). COLLECTION: David M. Koetser, New York. EXHIBITIONS: *Neapolitan Masters,* Finch College Museum of Art, New York, 1962, No. 21; *Art in Italy, 1600–1700,* The Detroit Institute of Arts, 1965, No. 150.

This sketch is a preparation for one of the scenes from the life of St. Catherine of Alexandria that Preti painted for the church of S. Pietro a Maiella in Naples between 1656 and 1661. The sketch deals with the climactic moment of the saint's terrestrial life, and we see her, flanked by the wheel on which she was tortured, kneeling in prayer behind her executioner. Preti gives us an oblique point of view that takes into account the high position of the picture in the church while accentuating the dramatic force of the composition by the rush of perspective. The lighting reinforces the focus on the central figures— the brutal executioner, the exalted, yielding St. Catherine, and the angel in the sky—guaranteeing their visibility to the congregation in the church. The more finished quality of these figures contrasts with the rest of the sketch, where Preti quickly tries out the setting and details: an abstract sky, weightless architecture, an anonymous ghostly crowd, and the visible changes in the position of the sword, which consequently seems to vibrate in the air. These very contrasts lend the scene a ghastly excitement, to modern eyes perhaps more fitting for the subject than the finish of the completed picture.

Preti's mature style is apparent in the sketch, especially in his peculiar combination of Caravaggesque lighting with a silvery tonality that derives from Veronese. The exceptional quality of the bozzetto indicates why the scenes from the life of St. Catherine mark a high point in Preti's work. Neapolitan artists were quick to learn from it, and Solimena acknowledged the power of this very composition by quoting it as a detail in his own great picture, *The Martyrdom of the Giustiniani* (Capodimonte, Naples).   J.K.

Lent by Robert and Bertina Suida Manning, New York

LUCA GIORDANO (1634–1705)

Called "Fa Presto" for his ability to paint rapidly, Giordano was a painter of overwhelming natural ability. He began painting in Naples under the influence of Ribera and then traveled all over Italy, visiting Rome, Bologna, Parma and Venice, assimilating the work of other artists as well as exerting his own style. He was court painter in Spain from 1692 to 1702 but returned to Naples in his last years. His works encompass all subjects, all sizes, and are of extraordinary quantity. Giordano was extremely influential, introducing the decorative painting of the 18th century and forming the broad ground on which the following generations built.

22. *SAINT LUKE PAINTING THE VIRGIN*. Oil on canvas. 18⅛ x 14¼ inches (47.5 x 36 cm). On back of frame: *Luca Giordano pinse*. EXHIBITION: F. Bologna, *Luca Giordano,* Galleria d'Arte "Il Carpine," Rome, 1966, No. 27. LITERATURE: O. Ferrari and G. Scavizzi, *Luca Giordano,* Naples, 1966, II, p. 227.

The subject of this sketch, St. Luke the Evangelist in the guise of the painter of the Virgin, is ancient and venerable. Though the massiveness of the figures and the density of the composition still tie this little work to the Baroque grand manner, the treatment is charming and intimate, showing Giordano as the precursor of the Rococo. No large-scale painting of this composition is known, but for reasons of style the sketch can be dated into the master's last period. The two oil sketches of 1704 of the story of Judith and Holofernes (City Art Museum of St. Louis) show similarly his free brush-stroke at the culminating point, while the airiness of color recalls his late fresco cycles in the Royal Palace in Madrid and elsewhere. These are the works which foreshadow the international style of eighteenth-century decoration.

The sketch is a brilliant example of the rapidity of execution for which Giordano was famous. The strokes of the drapery were applied with breathless speed, and a few touches suggest form. At the same time the lively surface handling is discreetly controlled by the simple but sophisticated structure of the composition. In this little sketch Giordano reveals his gift for effortless organization by a careful balancing of energy and stability.   J.K.

Lent by N. U. l'Architetto Andrea Busiri Vici, Rome

GIACOMO DEL PO (1659–1726)

Born in Rome and trained by his father, Del Po became a member of the Academy of Saint Luke at the age of 15. In 1683, he moved to Naples where he worked until his death. Formed within the style current in Rome in the 1670's, he turned from this to the Genoese painters Castiglione and Magnasco and the Neapolitans Giordano and Solimena. His late works became free and painterly, standing at the beginning of a Neapolitan Rococo.

23. *SKETCH FOR A CEILING IN THE PALAZZO DE MATTEI IN NAPLES.*
Oil on canvas. 40⅛ x 23⅝ inches (101 x 60 cm). EXHIBITION: *Mostra di bozzetti napoletani del seicento e del settecento,* Naples, 1947, No. 43. LITERATURE: R. Causa, *Pittura napoletana dal XV al XIX secolo,* Bergamo, 1957, p. 66, fig. 39; M. Picone, "Per la conoscenza del pittore Giacomo Del Po—II," *Bollettino d'Arte,* XLII, 1957, pp. 309–10, fig. 8.

This oil sketch with its small figures who gesture, turn and twist, brightly lit against a dark background, is an outstanding example of Del Po's mature style. The contrasts of light and dark are most striking; they are achieved with rapid strokes that produce the sensation of flickering light and movement across the canvas. A document of 1697 refers to Del Po's paintings "in a nocturnal manner" as something new in Naples and highly sought after by collectors (Prota-Giurleo, *Pittori napoletani del seicento,* Naples, 1953, p. 87). This "nocturnal" manner surely refers to the light-dark contrasts we see here and accords with Picone's dating of the work to 1700–05 (p. 316).

The glowing figures are carefully set within an architectural framework that opens in the center to reveal a celestial vision of goddesses and personifications of virtues who melt away in divine light. Outside the oval, at the ends of the main axes, are seated powerful figures personifying such qualities as fame, justice, and magnanimity. These surely refer to the De Mattei family. The flattering, allegorical language is in the old tradition, but the evanescent lights and jewel-like colors create a new world that is Del Po's own, unexpected in Naples. One may detect the influences of Castiglione and Magnasco in this work, but they are subsumed in a personal style that places Del Po among the most original and imaginative of decorative painters in Italy.   J.K.

Lent by the Museo Nazionale di San Martino, Naples

FRANCESCO SOLIMENA (1657–1747)

Solimena carefully studied the work of Giordano and was his successor on the artistic scene in Naples. His dark shadows and accentuated contours reveal the strong impression made on him by Lanfranco and Preti. Aside from a trip to Rome in 1700, Solimena remained in Naples all his life. By the 1720's his work was sought after all over Europe, due to the strong appeal of his large compositions of overstated drama. He set up an academy that became the center of artistic life in Naples and produced his own successor, Francesco De Mura.

24. *ST. VINCENT FERRER*. Oil on canvas. 28 x 22⅝ inches (71 x 58 cm).

St. Vincent Ferrer was a Spanish Dominican of the 14th century, famous for winning many converts by his persuasive preaching. We see him here as the preacher who warns of the Last Judgment, dressed in the Dominican habit, holding an open book of sermons, and pointing upwards to the judge of all men. The Saint's gesture is supported by an angel who, sounding a trumpet, symbolically announces the coming of the Last Day. Divine approbation is also shown by the Saint's large wings, referring to the fact that the pope had compared him to an angel sent by God to convert sinners.

This sketch may be dated *circa* 1710, the date of the finished picture, (F. Bologna, *Francesco Solimena*, Naples, 1958, p. 255). With its strong contrasts of light and dark, it is fully representative of Solimena's style. The habit of the saint is partly filled with deep shadows, and the strong chiaroscuro creates an image at once fluid and sculpturesque. The light, coming from no single source, is manipulated for its dramatic possibilities. Forms are simplified into geometric shapes, for instance the shoes and the gesturing hand. Even in this single full-length figure, Solimena reveals his penchant for high drama, placing the saint in an isolated and desolate spot and charging him with a striking seriousness and emotion. Such interpretation, characteristic of Solimena's work, made him the undisputed master of Neapolitan painting after Luca Giordano.

The finished painting of this subject, of almost the exact size as the sketch, is in the Hermitage in Leningrad (Katalog *Kartinnoĭ Gallerei Ermitazh,* Petrograd, 1912, I, p. 240). There is also another oil sketch of this same subject and size in the National Gallery in Warsaw (*Malarstwo Wloskie w Zbiorach Polskich XVII–XVIIIw* [Mostra della pittura italiana nelle collezioni polacche XVII–XVIII sec.], Warsaw, 1956, fig. 95 [as St. Thomas Aquinas]).   J.K.

Lent by Sig. M. C. Viezzoli, Genoa

FRANCESCO DE MURA (1696–1794)

De Mura was the most important student of Solimena, and his work was very popular in Naples and in Turin, where he was court painter from 1741 to 1743. His main center of activity was Naples, but he received commissions from many other places. He carried his own version of Solimena's style into large decorative cycles, such as that in the Royal Palace in Turin, painted in the light and airy colors that one associates with the 18th century. He was also a well-known portrait painter. Due to his strong ties with Solimena, he never developed a Rococo style, but in his last phase turned to a rather dry classicism.

25. *THE INVESTITURE OF CARLOMAN.* Oil on canvas. 24¼ x 18¼ inches (61.5 x 46.5 cm). In the lower right-hand corner is written *del Muro* and an illegible abbreviation, probably an *f* for *fecit.* COLLECTION: P. and D. Colnaghi & Co., Ltd., London. LITERATURE: *Burlington Magazine,* CIV, 1962, p. xii (ill.).

The subject of this work is extremely rare. It shows Carloman, son of Charles Martel and joint ruler of the Frankish kingdom, receiving the cassock in 747 upon giving up his crown and scepter, symbol of his position as Mayor of the Palace, to embrace a monastic life. He entered the monastery at Monte Cassino, where a chapel was later dedicated to him and for which De Mura received the painting commission (B. De Dominici, *Vite de' pittori . . . napoletani,* 1742–5, III, p. 696; and R. Enggass, "Francesco De Mura alla Nunziatella," *Bollettino d'Arte,* XLIX, 1964, p. 146, n. 7).

According to an early description of the chapel of Carloman, the main picture showing Pope Zaccaria placing the habit of the monastic order on the sainted king was painted by De Mura (*Descrizione istorica del sacro real monistero di Monte Cassino. . . ,* Naples, 1751, p. 60). The present oil sketch must certainly be preparatory for this painting, which was destroyed during the last war. The sketch is not dated, but we do know that the relics of Carloman were transferred from the high altar to his chapel in the period 1732–34 (*Descrizione istorica. . . ,* p. 60; and D. P. Guillaume, *Descrizione istorica e artistica di Monte Cassino,* 1879, p. 122), and this would be a fitting moment to commission major decorations for the chapel.

This tentative dating in the early 1730's is also supported by stylistic analysis and comparison with dated works. This painting, carried to a relatively high degree of finish for an oil sketch, reveals a clear contrast of light and dark areas and a fairly static organization of color across the canvas; the same shade of violet or yellow, for example, recurs in various parts of the work, creating an over-all balance of color. The composition is fairly symmetrical, directing our eyes toward the youthful Carloman, and by gesture and glance the figures help to focus our attention onto the kneeling protagonist. De Mura's sketch for *The Adoration of the Magi* of 1732, in the Pio Monte della Misericordia in Naples, is similar in style and composition (Enggass, p. 135, fig. 3). The figures belong to the same repertory, such as the bald-headed acolyte in voluminous robes and the portrait-like man standing to the right. The agitated putti above and the similarity of color and of contrasts of light and dark in both sketches suggest that they belong to the same period. For these reasons, this oil sketch may be dated in the early 1730's and may be seen as an example of the first phase of De Mura's activity, when he was beginning to receive important commissions and establish himself as one of the leading decorative painters of Naples, alongside his teacher Solimena.   J.K.

Lent by Mr. and Mrs. Milton J. Lewine, New York

GENOA

BERNARDO STROZZI (1581–1644)

Strozzi began his career in the studio of the Sienese Mannerist Pietro Sorri. Sensitive to foreign painters in Genoa, Strozzi reacted favorably to the Lombard masters Cerano and G. C. Procaccini and to the work of Orazio Gentileschi, from whom he derived his early dark Caravaggesque manner, as well as to the styles of Rubens and van Dyck. Under their influence his palette lightened. Strozzi's personal life was complex. Having become a Capuchin at the age of seventeen, he left the monastery in 1610 to become a prelate. Refusing to return to the monastery, he was imprisoned and upon his release fled to Venice, in 1630. There, influenced by the work of Giovanni Lys and Domenico Fetti, Strozzi lightened his palette still further and developed a vibrant color and a freedom of brush-stroke that, in turn, influenced Venetian painting.

26. *HORATIUS COCLES DEFENDING THE BRIDGE.* Oil on paper mounted on canvas. 9½ x 14 inches (24 x 35.5 cm). EXHIBITIONS:*Unbekante Schönheit,* Kunsthaus, Zurich, 1956, No. 247; *Italian Art and Britain,* Royal Academy, London, 1960, No. 388; *Genoese Masters—Cambiaso to Magnasco,* Dayton Art Institute, The Ringling Museum at Sarasota, The Wadsworth Atheneum at Hartford, 1962–63, No. 52. LITERATURE:G. Fiocco, *Bernardo Strozzi,* Rome, 1921, pl. 1.

This is a preliminary study for Strozzi's ceiling fresco in the Palazzo Carpaneto (formerly Centurione) at San Pier d'Arena near Genoa. The fresco is traditionally dated to Strozzi's early period, *circa* 1623–25, on the basis of statements made by his early biographers. The subject is an episode from the life of the legendary Roman hero Horatius Cocles, who defended the Sublician bridge against the Etruscan army of Lars Porsena while his own Roman soldiers destroyed the bridge behind him. For all that the sketch is painted so freely and vivaciously, the *pentimenti* show that Strozzi paid great attention to the clear presentation of conflict and battle. Cocles' shield, originally held up behind his head, was placed in front of him, bringing the two generals into more direct contact. The idea is carried further in the fresco where Cocles' shield is again slightly altered while the Etruscan's shield, now rectangular, is paralleled with that of Cocles. Many similar changes were made in the final version, all of them relatively minor but involving a general tightening of the composition and a heightening of the drama.

Despite the mannerist echoes in the grouping of figures, this bozzetto, with its golden light and glowing tonality, documents the change in Strozzi's palette and handling of paint in the period between 1620 and 1630 when, still in Genoa, he came under the influence of Venetian painting as seen through Flemish eyes.   P.M.E.

Lent by Mr. Denis Mahon, London

VALERIO CASTELLO (1624–1659)

Valerio Castello, son of the local Mannerist painter Bernardo, spent his entire short career in Genoa aside from trips to Milan and Parma. As a student he worked for a short time with Domenico Fiasella and Giovanni Andrea de Ferrari, from whom he learned that rich combination of Tuscan, Milanese, and Flemish elements then current in Genoese art. Valerio's interest in coloristic effects and chiaroscuro reveal the influence of Venetian painting seen through Rubens and van Dyck and of the work of G. B. Procaccini. A master of both easel and fresco painting, Valerio established a tradition of fresco decoration in Genoa carried on by his pupils Domenico Piola and Gregorio de Ferrari, and developed a free, highly expressive painterly manner whose heritage is seen in the work of Alessandro Magnasco.

27. *TOBIAS AND THE ANGEL.* Oil on canvas. 18½ x 21½ inches (47 x 55 cm). COLLECTION: G. B. Moro. LITERATURE: None. For the artist, see B. Riccio, "Contributo a Valerio Castello," *Commentari,* VIII, 1957, pp. 369–378 (with references).

Valerio Castello's *œuvre,* produced in the brief span of about twelve years, presents problems of chronology. Since there are only three firmly dated paintings, an altarpiece of 1648 and two works of 1655, stylistic criteria must remain the basis for his chronology. Valerio's work can be tentatively grouped into three phases: an early period *circa* 1646–9, represented by scenes from the life of S. Giacomo in the Oratory of S. Giacomo alla Marina; a middle phase *circa* 1649–55, to which belongs a study for the *Miracle of St. Zita* in the Palazzo Bianco in Genoa; and a late phase *circa* 1655–9. Apparently, these three periods are defined by changes in the relative size of the figures in the compositions. In the middle period the figures are relatively large in size, compared with works of the early and late phases.

Our sketch of *Tobias and the Angel* evidently belongs to the middle period since it is worked out with large figures whose action can be easily read as it unfolds across the picture plane. There is here a breadth and freedom of handling and a sense of openness that derives from the comparatively luminous palette and the sharply accentuated light. One does not see here the Correggesque sfumato that in other, perhaps later, paintings almost completely dissolves the forms. This fact also suggests a date *circa* 1649–51 because Soprani, by implication, places Valerio's Parmese trip rather late in his career, probably in the 1650's.

In this sketch, drapery is used for expressive purpose. The graceful, undulating, almost ribbon-like movements combine with the elegance of the figures and the lightness of color to give the sketch a sense of what Briganti calls the 'proto-Rococo' found in Valerio's mature works. Drapery is here divorced from absolute adherence to natural laws but still has a sense of cloth, unlike the drapery in Valerio's late work where everything becomes totally dematerialized; in the *Tobias* linear rhythms are elegant and fluid rather than emotionally supercharged. And the hands and feet, characteristically for Valerio's sketches, taper away to delicate points.

The picture for which the *Tobias* was made is unknown, but we know from other examples that Valerio used his sketches as records to which he could later return, and no final painting may ever have been made.   P.M.E.

Lent Anonymously

GIOVANNI BENEDETTO CASTIGLIONE, called
IL GRECHETTO (1600/10–1665)

Although Castiglione began his artistic career in Genoa, he worked largely outside the city, making trips to Florence, Bologna, Naples and probably Venice. He was in Rome by 1632 and at least by 1648—perhaps as early as 1639—he was working as court painter in Mantua; after 1661 he divided his time between Mantua and Genoa. His work reveals the lasting impact of the Flemish or Flemish-influenced painters active in Genoa, Sinibaldo Scorza and Jan Roos in his fondness for pastoral themes involving numerous animals, and Rubens and van Dyck for his style. In addition, as his graphic work testifies, he was acquainted with Rembrandt's etchings as early as 1630–34. In his later years Castiglione emerged as a leader of the Baroque in Genoa.

28. *SHEPHERDS AND FLOCKS*. Oil on paper. 10½ x 18½ inches (26.8 x 47.2 cm). COLLECTIONS: Zaccaria Sagredo; Consul Smith. LITERATURE: Anthony Blunt, *The Drawings of G. B. Castiglione and Stefano della Bella at Windsor Castle,* London, 1954, No. 120.

This free and brilliant study is one of a group that Blunt dates 1640 to 1645 on the basis of comparison with pen drawings and etchings. The subject relates to Castiglione's earlier caravan paintings, but also shows the expansion of his repertory after he came into contact with the Poussin circle in Rome and their mythological and arcadian themes.

Castiglione's technical versatility and love of experiment—he was the inventor of the monotype—is revealed in this kind of sketch, which breaks down the barrier between drawing and painting. Using no binding medium, he mixes directly on his brush a coarsely ground pigment with linseed oil, adding more oil for transparent areas and less for opaque effects, much in the manner of a water-colorist. He thus developed the art of the oil brush drawing or sketch into a medium of great fluency and direct appeal. In this sketch the tones, handled as in a water-color, are combined with firm, often dry, brush strokes. The artist translates the firm hatching lines of his early pen drawings into a more fluid brush medium which gives the whole a painterly, picturesque effect. This sketch, like so many of Castiglione's, does not seem to have been made with a specific painting in view.   P.M.E.

Lent by gracious permission of Her Majesty Queen Elizabeth II, from The Royal Library, Windsor Castle

29. *CHRIST ON THE CROSS.* Oil on paper. 10⅜ x 15½ inches (26.4 x 39.6 cm). Numbered in pencil "44" and in ink "26" (?). COLLECTIONS: Zaccaria Sagredo; Consul Smith. EXHIBITIONS: *Seventeenth Century Art in Europe,* Royal Academy, London, 1938, No. 468; Royal Academy, London, 1950, No. 398. LITERATURE: A. Blunt, "The Drawings of G. B. Castiglione," *Journal of the Warburg and Courtauld Inst.,* VIII, 1945, p. 171; A. Blunt, *The Drawings of G. B. Castiglione and Stefano della Bella at Windsor Castle,* London, 1954, No. 192.

Here line is less important than in Castiglione's earlier sketches, such as the *Shepherds and Flocks* above; now we see a sketch planned in color from its inception. The modeling of the forms is done with opaque pigment pre-mixed with a binding medium in the more traditional manner. The sketch is executed in Castiglione's highly emotional late style, in which tones and the tensely executed line and drapery move according to their own inner life to dissolve form.

Castiglione does not use the traditional iconography of the Crucifixion but depicts what Blunt calls a contemplation on the theme, which includes the mourning figures of Mary and John, angels in the sky, and a group of despairing men at the left. Blunt suggests that these may be Jews begging for forgiveness, while Bernheimer (*Art Bull.,* XXXIII, 1951, pp. 47–51) identifies them as figures of saints and prophets.

The sketch is evocative and moving in a way that would seem to make it unique, but the Crucifixion was a theme dear to Castiglione, and this sketch is related to four other sketches (two at Windsor Castle, one at the Rhode Island School of Design, and one in the Costa Collection, Genoa), a painting in the Palazzo Bianco at Genoa, a monotype, and several drawings. Of all these, the sketch shown here is closest to the Costa sketch, which also includes the figures at the foot of the Cross; but it would seem to be the culminating synthesis of the entire series, unique in its iconography, evanescent lighting, and horizontal format. Blunt dates this study *circa* 1655–60; it appears to be close to 1660, just preceding Castiglione's ultimate phase.   P.M.E.

Lent by gracious permission of Her Majesty Queen Elizabeth II, from The Royal Library, Windsor Castle

NORTH ITALIAN SCHOOLS

ANTONIO D'ENRICO, called TANZIO DA VARALLO
(1574/80–1635)

Following in the local tradition of Gaudenzio Ferrari, Tanzio worked from about 1616 to 1628 at the Sacro Monte of Varallo, a site where painting and sculpture were combined in a popular art form which kept alive the spirit of medieval mystery plays. Sometime between 1610 and 1615 he must have been in Rome, where he felt the impact of Caravaggio's work. Active as a painter in both oil and fresco, Tanzio throughout his career grafted a forceful realism upon the Lombard late Mannerist style of his contemporaries, G. C. Procaccini, Cerano and Morazzone, creating an intense, highly personal manner that is permeated by the mystical tendencies so characteristic of Lombard painting of the early seventeenth century.

30. *THE BATTLE OF SENNACHERIB.* Oil on canvas. 59 x 36 inches (153 x 90 cm). COLLECTION: Contessa Luisa Avogadro Ferrari Ardicini, Novara. EXHIBITIONS: *Mostra del Caravaggio e dei caravaggeschi,* Milan, Palazzo Reale, 1951, No. 170; *Mostra della pittura italiana del seicento e del settecento,* S. Paolo, Brazil, and Rio de Janeiro, 1954; *Mostra del manierismo piemontese e lombardo del seicento,* Turin, Palazzo Madama, 1955, and Ivrea, Centro Culturale Olivetti, 1955, No. 41; *Mostra del Tanzio da Varallo,* Turin, Palazzo Madama, 1959, No. 17, pls. 95–96; *Mostra del Tanzio da Varallo,* Varallo, Museo Civico, 1960; *Mostra del barocco piemontese,* Turin, 1963, II, No. 20; *Le Caravage et la peinture italienne du XVIIe siècle,* Musée du Louvre, Paris, 1965, No. 112.

This monochrome oil sketch is a preparatory study for Tanzio's large canvas of *The Battle of Sennacherib* in the Chapel of the Guardian Angel in the Church of S. Gaudenzio at Novara (Pl. 30A). The Nazzarini family also commissioned Tanzio to paint frescoes in the Chapel, and the bozzetto as well as the much larger final version can be dated 1627–29 on the basis of both the signed and dated contract for the commission and the inscription in the chapel itself. Tanzio illustrated a story taken from the Book of Kings. During the reign of Hezekiah, King of Judah, Sennacherib, King of Assyria, took the cities of Judah. Hezekiah prayed to the Lord, Who sent an Avenging Angel to smite the Assyrians in their camp. The choice of the subject can be regarded as a manifestation of the counter-reformatory spirit against the threat of penetration of ideas from the Protestant North. Portraying the most dramatic moment in the narrative, Tanzio shows the Angel of the Lord coming down from the sky while the Assyrian army struggles below.

The most significant change from the bozzetto to the finished painting involves the Caravaggesque figure of the Angel who, in the study, flies down from the sky in a sharply foreshortened view, while in the finished work he is turned into a sturdy, upright figure who bursts through the clouds. The format of the painting in the chapel is much narrower and much more elongated than that of the bozzetto, and the part played by the soldiers and the Angel has been exchanged: while the Avenging Angel is the principal figure of the finished work, the main weight of the sketch is concentrated on the fleeing soldiers. It is these ghostly soldiers that give the sketch its terrific punch. The contorted bodies, awkward anatomy and the confusion in the brittle forms, combined with the almost terrifying realism of the fallen man whose body seems to extend beyond the frontal plane of the canvas, results in a work typical of Tanzio's tremendously powerful late style.

P.M.E.

Lent by the Banca Popolare di Novara

ALESSANDRO MAGNASCO, called LISSANDRINO
(1667–1749)

Magnasco, Genoese by birth, spent most of his career in Milan (from *circa* 1680 on), where he studied under the painter Filippo Abbiati and came into contact with the works of Cerano, Morazzone, and Sebastiano Ricci. He began as a portrait painter, but soon developed the type of picture with small figures in landscape settings for which he is best known. Apart from short trips, Magnasco worked in Florence as court painter to Grand Duke Cosimo III from about 1703 until 1711 when he returned to Milan for twenty-four years; finally, in 1735, he went home to Genoa and remained there until his death. His dark canvases are peopled with gypsies, soldiers and monks—types set apart from the rest of society—and are allied essentially to the Baroque rather than the Rococo. Heir to Valerio Castello in his freedom of stroke and to Castiglione in his personal and romantic piety, Magnasco is both *retardataire* in his dark palette and *avant-garde* in the fluid technique he employs to describe an hallucinatory world. The advent of modern Expressionism has led to a re-evaluation of his tortured visions, emotionally accessible to our own times.

31. *DYING SOLDIER.* Oil on panel. 20 x 11 inches (51 x 28 cm). EXHIBITIONS: *Mostra di pittori genovesi del seicento e del settecento,* Genoa, 1938, No. 113; *Mostra del Magnasco,* Genoa, 1949, No. 60. LITERATURE: G. Delogu, *Pittori minori liguri, lombardi, e piemontese del seicento e settecento,* Venice, 1931, pl. 192.

32. *BURIAL OF A SOLDIER.* Oil on panel. 20 x 11 inches (51 x 28 cm). EXHIBITION: *Mostra del Magnasco,* Genoa, 1949, No. 61. LITERATURE: G. Delogu, *loc. cit.*

These two monochrome oil studies, relating consecutive moments in a narrative, are unusual in Magnasco's *oeuvre:* we know of only one other work executed on panel rather than canvas (an *Adoration of the Magi* in Venice, *Mostra,* 1949, No. 75) and of almost no other works that look like preparations rather than small, finished, sketchy pictures. Here forms can be read only as light and dark; one reacts immediately to the thick impasto of the pigment itself, scumbled onto the panel in a furor of activity. Unconcerned with problems of spatial structure, Magnasco defined his compositions in such broad sweeps of pigment that at first glance his distortions of anatomy and facial expression are lost in the perception of the whole as an abstract study.

Dating these sketches is difficult. Documents are of little help with Magnasco, and he himself signed few works and dated only two. Morassi dates the bozzetti *circa* 1710–1715, to the beginning of Magnasco's second Milanese period, before he reduced the size of his figures and concentrated on flickering light. Although Magnasco may have been only in his early 30's when he painted these sketches, they show a mature concentration of pictorial means in presenting a grim world of death and destruction. He goes beyond his heritage of Genoese brushstroke and Lombard mysticism in separating pictorial from representational function, creating a tense, phantasmagoric world that remains a very private vision.

Magnasco had scattered imitators but no real students, for his style, like Caravaggio's, could not be taught. Spiritually linked to earlier artists like Rosa or Callot, he can be seen as the ancestor of contemporary Expressionism. P.M.E.

Lent by the Pinacoteca Malaspina, Pavia

CARLO INNOCENZO CARLONI (1686–1775)

The son of the architect Giovanni Battista Carloni, Carlo was born at Scaria and went early in his career to Venice. Later he worked at the French Academy in Rome. Like Sebastiano Ricci a generation before, he was soon drawn north, and from 1707 to 1733 he received a number of major commissions in Austria, southern Germany and Switzerland. Eventually he returned to northern Italy, remaining in the north where he died in 1775. He was the master of a loose but fluidly dynamic stroke and some 300 bozzetti were found in his studio after his death.

33. *THE SACRIFICE OF IPHIGENIA*. Oil on canvas. 16¾ x 27½ inches (42.5 x 69.8 cm). COLLECTION: S. L. Forwood, London. EXHIBITION: *Paintings by Old Masters,* P. D. Colnaghi and Co., Ltd., London, 1965, No. 16. LITERATURE: F. Lechi, "Un elenco di abbozzi delle opere di Carlo Carloni," *Arte Lombarda,* X, 1965, pp. 133–4.

The pathetic story of Iphigenia is shown here by Carloni in vigorous and intense dramatic terms. In the middle of the composition the artist has placed a stepped altar on which Iphigenia lies. As the design is evidently for an upper wall or ceiling, the eye level of the spectator is at the base of the altar, but his attention is directed up to the body of the heroine. Directly behind, her father Agamemnon, about to plunge the sacrificial knife into her body, looks up to the goddess Artemis. The story has two different endings: in one version Iphigenia is actually killed, while in another she is borne away by Artemis and a hind is sacrificed in her place. Carloni has chosen the most exciting moment by leaving Iphigenia's fate still unresolved.

The attribution of the picture speaks for itself. The firm figures, loose and fiery brushstroke and strongly contrasted lights and shadows are characteristic of Carloni's style. There is in addition documentary evidence. An inventory of the sketches found in his studio after Carloni's death was published by his son when he offered them for sale (Lechi). Under the heading *Opere profane, isthoriche, e favolose, Quadri* is listed a *Sacrifice of Iphigenia* measuring 8 *once* by 1 *braccio, 2 once.* Conversion of the Milanese measurements into centimeters gives us only a minimal difference in height and there can be little doubt that our sketch is the one listed in Carloni's studio. The rubric *Quadri* points to a sketch for an independent painting in oil on canvas, but the composition implies a mural decoration, and Carloni's son may simply have classified the sketch incorrectly.

Dr. K. Garas has suggested in a letter that the sketch is a preparatory study for part of a ceiling in Schloss Ludwigsburg near Stuttgart. Carloni worked there *ca.* 1731–1733, and he may have valued the sketch as a record of his work or as a possible model for later compositions since he kept it with him till his death. But the tenacious preservation of sketches was in fact Carloni's standard procedure and accounts for the extraordinary number of 300 bozzetti found in his Como studio. (A copy of the list, dated 1786, is in the library of Mr. Janos Scholz, New York; the list is more complete than the one published by Lechi.)

D.M.

Lent by Mr. and Mrs. David E. Rust, Washington, D.C.

34. *GOD THE FATHER RECEIVING THE MADONNA OF THE IMMAC- ULATE CONCEPTION.* Oil on canvas. 38¾ x 30⁵⁄₁₆ inches (97.2 x 77 cm). COLLECTION: John Gellatly. LITERATURE: National Collection of Fine Arts, Smith-

sonian Institution, *Catalog of American and European Paintings in the Gellatly Collection,* Washington, 1945, No. 135 (attributed to Tiepolo); F. Lechi, "Un elenco di abozzi delle opere di Carlo Carloni," *Arte Lombarda,* X, 1965, pp. 127-8.

This is a bozzetto for the cupola of a church, showing God the Father just below mid-center, receiving the Virgin Mary into Heaven. Grouped around the central figures are crowds of angels, massed in loose, concentric ovals. At the Virgin's feet is her crescent moon, and under the *orbis mundi* the vanquished Serpent writhes in frustration. The brush strokes are quick and the composition is dramatized by simple juxtapositions of light and shade. The hand of a disciplined master is easily seen in the firm modeling and the careful arrangement of the tiers of angels, all focusing on God the Father and the Virgin while at the same time suggesting the infinity of Heaven. The painted rim of the dome appears in the left-hand corner, but not enough is shown to define the perimeter as a circle or an oval. The oculus, apparently held up at the center by putti, has a distinctly oval shape, so that the artist may have intended to decorate an oval cupola.

As late as 1945 the sketch was given to Tiepolo, but the recent attribution to Carloni seems convincing. Moreover, the title of a sketch recorded in Carloni's studio—listed among works done for churches—fits the description of our sketch: *Il Padre Eterno in atto di ricevere la Vergine Immacolata, Angeli, che scacciano il Serpente* (Lechi), but the converted measurements, 60 x 70 cm, do not. Yet if these measurements reverse width and height, the sketch in Carloni's studio had the same proportions as ours and may thus have been a second version related to the same unknown commission.

In style the sketch seems typical of the earlier Carloni ceilings in Austria, comparable with his cupolas in the chapel of the Belvedere Palace in Vienna, *ca.* 1733, and in the parish church at Gross Siegharts, *ca.* 1727. In these cupolas Carloni swirls a multitude of active figures in a space dramatized by light and shade. The glowing lights, sometimes falling direct and sometimes piercing banks of clouds, unify the compositions. All these characteristics allow us to assign our sketch to the decade 1720 to 1730.   D.M.

Lent by the National Collection of Fine Arts, Smithsonian Institution

GIUSEPPE BAZZANI (1690–1769)

Bazzani, born in Mantua, studied with the mediocre Cadioli and Canti of Parma; he also studied the works of old masters, particularly those of 16th-century Venice, and learned from a number of artists nearer his time (Maffei, Magnasco, etc.), but in no way that can be easily summed up. He was a solitary artist and lived his working life in Mantua, where his style matured around 1740. During his last years he was crippled and ailing, and it was probably at this time that Francesco Raineri, called Lo Schivenoglia, collaborated with him. He had almost no followers in Italy, but his work appealed to Austrian painters, particularly to Maulbertsch.

35. *A BODY CARRIED TO ITS GRAVE.* Oil on paper mounted on canvas. 24½ x 15 inches (62 x 38 cm).

36. *A SOUL LED TO HEAVEN BY AN ANGEL.* Oil on paper mounted on canvas. 24½ x 15 inches (62 x 38 cm). COLLECTION: Contini Bonacossi, Florence. EXHIBITION: N. Ivanoff, *Mostra del Bazzani,* Mantua, 1950, Nos. 67, 61. LITERATURE: N. Ivanoff, "Bazzani, la mostra di Mantova," *Emporium,* CXI, 1950, pp. 204–5; and "Mostra del Bazzani a Mantova," *Bollettino d'Arte,* XXXV, 1950, p. 377; C. Perina, "Some Unpublished Paintings by Giuseppe Bazzani," *Art Bulletin,* XLVI, 1964, p. 230.

These two sketches belong to a group of four (all Kress Collection, New York), the others being a *Man on His Death Bed,* protected by Christ from demons, and a *Scene of Hell,* where a man and a woman are tortured by demons. The iconography of the set has sometimes been confused. The two scenes of death and burial, for example, have been paired as a death and burial of St. Joseph (e.g., Perina, p. 230), and the scene showing the ascension of the soul has in the past been called *The Assumption of the Virgin* or *The Assumption of Mary Magdalen.* Yet the four paintings ought to be considered as a set, a kind of allegorical biography of death and the after-life of the human soul: the good soul dies in Christ, the body of the bad soul is hastened off to burial, the good soul ascends to heaven, the souls of the evil are punished in hell. Supporting evidence for this interpretation is only indirect but points in this direction. In 1760 Thaddeus Stammel carved a set of wood sculptures in the library of the monastery at

Admont in Austria. They represent *The Pilgrim's Death, The Last Judgment, Hell,* and *Heaven;* only the *Heaven* has any similarity with Bazzani's analogous sketch, but the date, the influence of Bazzani on Austrian art, and the unusual character of the subjects are suggestive for the meaning of Bazzani's sketches.

The iconography cannot be divorced from Bazzani's personal style and private devotion. He was a celibate and intensely religious, a believer, according to Ivanoff, in quietism, that mystic movement that sought contact with God through the immediate inspiration of the individual conscience and advocated a kind of exalted passiveness of the soul in contemplation. We may detect echoes of quietism in Bazzani's sketches, where the embodied soul performs no action of its own but is passively acted upon, whether tossed away like refuse or lifted into the empyrean.

The icy lighting and nervous brushwork, deriving from Bencovich, heighten the emotionalism, expressed equally by the angular forms of the bodies and poses. The rapidity and sureness with which these sketches were painted are also encountered in Bazzani's finished productions, but, except for a few ovals, these scenes are smaller than any other of Bazzani's known work. This, together with the technique of oil grisaille painting on paper, point up the character of these scenes as sketches, preparations for works of about 1750 that are still unknown.

M.C.A.

Lent by Mrs. Rush Kress, New York

VENICE

DOMENICO FETTI (*circa* 1589–1623)

Domenico Fetti, trained in Rome with the early-Baroque painter Cigoli, also came into contact with the landscapist Elsheimer and Caravaggio's followers. In Mantua by about 1613 as Court Painter and Inspector of Galleries to Duke Ferdinando II, Fetti studied Rubens and the sixteenth-century Venetian masters in the Gonzaga Collection. Although he painted court portraits and frescoes, Fetti preferred small canvases; he is most famous for the numerous illustrations of Parables he did in both Mantua and Venice. While working in Mantua, Fetti made trips to Florence in 1618 and to Venice in 1621, where he returned in 1622 and remained until his death. With his loose brush-stroke and luminous color, Fetti, together with Lys and Strozzi, helped revive Venetian painting.

37. *DAVID WITH THE HEAD OF GOLIATH*. Oil on canvas. 20 x 15 inches (51 x 38 cm). COLLECTION: Marchese del Carretto. EXHIBITION: (P. Zampetti), *La pittura del seicento a Venezia,* Venice, 1959, No. 51. LITERATURE: A. Podestà, "Il seicento a Venezia," *Emporium,* CXXX, 1959, pp. 100–102; P. Grate, *Konstens Venedig,* Stockholm, 1962, p. 117. Grate says that this sketch was acquired in Venice; is this then the picture recorded by J. Burckhardt, *Der Cicerone,* Leipzig, 1869, III, p. 1067, as the "rudely represented . . . [David] sitting on Goliath's head," in the Palazzo Manfrin, Venice? (For the Hampton Court *David,* see M. Levey, *The Later Italian Pictures in the Collection of Her Majesty the Queen,* London, 1964, No. 469. For the Dresden *David,* see M. Endres Soltmann, *Domenico Fetti* (dissertation), Munich, 1914, p. 45; H. Posse, *Die Staatliche Gemäldegalerie zu Dresden,* Dresden, 1929, No. 415; K. Steinbart, *Johann Liss,* Berlin, 1940, p. 183; C. Perina, *Mantova: le arti,* Mantua, 1965, III, pp. 456–457. References and discussion very kindly supplied in a letter by Professor Pamela Askew, who is inclined, without commitment and subject to review, to agree with Steinbart in placing the Dresden picture well into Fetti's Mantuan years, perhaps as late as *circa* 1619–1622.)

David sits on a rock before a summarily defined landscape. In the clear emphasis he gives to the sword and the head of Goliath, Fetti conceives the subject as image rather than as narrative, a typical approach in his early works. Although the type of David with his feather beret is Caravaggesque in its trappings, color and form owe more to such Venetians as Jacopo Bassano, Tintoretto and Veronese.

Fetti's chronology is problematic: dated paintings are rare, his career was relatively brief, and the time span between stylistic developments may be short. But this bozzetto is clearly later than his Roman works with their harder contours. By virtue of its soft silver-gray tones, pale color, luminous atmosphere and dissolving of contours, the sketch seems characteristic of Fetti's Mantuan works; additionally typical are the twisted, elongated brush-strokes that define the folds of David's garments. In nascent form such strokes appear in a grisaille of *circa* 1614–1621 (A. Rizzi, *Arte Veneta,* XVII, 1963, pp. 182–183), where we also find David's facial type—plump, with a pointed nose and high, heavy eyelids. The type derives from Barocci and Bassano and tends to disappear from Fetti's later paintings. The date of the sketch would thus be *circa* 1616–1620. But this dating is offered only cautiously. Zampetti and Podestà, for example, think that the sketch belongs to Fetti's very last years.

Fetti executed several versions of the *David,* but the sketch is closest to the painting in Dresden (No. 415; 160 x 112 cm), much closer than to the large version (replica?) at Hampton Court (Levey, No. 469), which shows many minor variations, for instance, in David's pose and the design of the sword hilt. The Dresden picture, executed in warm brownish tones with a red accent in the beret, is more detailed than the sketch, and the background includes Goliath's decapitated body and figures of fleeing Philistines. Although Fetti often made replicas of his paintings, including the *David,* for private patrons, our sketch has none of the qualities of a replica and should be regarded as a bozzetto, or possibly a modello, for the Dresden work. Second versions of Fetti's Parables are often more freely handled than the original (P. Askew, *Art Bulletin,* XLIII, 1961, p. 34), but the question does not arise here, where narrative is absent and the format differs as between bozzetto and execution.   P.M.E.

Lent by Sig. M. P. Viezzoli, Genoa

SEBASTIANO RICCI (1659–1734)

Ricci was born in Belluno and began his career studying such earlier Bolognese masters as Lodovico Carracci and Guido Reni. He later came under the influence of Pietro da Cortona and Luca Giordano. Throughout his life he traveled extensively, working in Rome, Florence, Bologna, Vienna, Paris and London. Late in his life he returned to Italy and died in Venice in 1734.

38. *ASSUMPTION OF THE VIRGIN.* Oil on canvas. 54¾ x 28¼ inches (139 x 72.3 cm). COLLECTIONS: Count Mapelli, Bergamo; Jacob H. Heimann, New York. EXHIBITIONS: *Four Centuries of Venetian Painting,* Toledo Museum of Art, 1940, No. 42; *Italian Baroque Painting of the 17th and 18th Centuries,* Vassar College Art Gallery, Poughkeepsie, 1940, No. 26; *Italian Baroque Painting,* California Palace of the Legion of Honor, San Francisco, 1941, No. 95; *Flight, Fantasy, Faith, Fact,* Dayton Art Institute, 1953–1954, No. 99; *Madonna in Art,* Fine Arts Gallery of San Diego, 1957, No. 35; *Christmas Exhibition,* Roberson Memorial

Center, Binghamton, New York, 1959; *Sebastiano and Marco Ricci in America*, Brooks Memorial Art Gallery, Memphis, 1965–1966, and The University of Kentucky Art Gallery, Lexington, 1966, No. 12. LITERATURE: J. von Derschau, *Sebastiano Ricci*, Heidelberg, 1922, pp. 54–55; *Museum of Fine Arts Bulletin*, Springfield, Mass., XI, Feb.–March, 1945, Nos. 5 and 6.

The painting shown here is a preparatory sketch of the type called a modello, the final stage of design made for inspection by the patrons. The sketch was made for an altarpiece in the church of S. Giovanni Battista in Clusone near Bergamo, painted during Ricci's stay in Milan about 1695 (von Derschau, p. 54). The final composition exactly follows that of the sketch with but one variation, the shifting of the glance of the putto under the Madonna's right knee down towards the center. This small change reinforces the compositional cohesiveness of the picture: it is the kind of refinement of vision that takes place in the development from a sketch to a finished work, dispelling all doubts that the sketch may be a replica made after the altarpiece.

Compared with the finished picture, the modello is painted with a loose and fluid vibrancy that animates the groups of figures. These are divided into two tiers separated by a bright band of sky, a device learned by Ricci from the Bolognese masters of the early 17th century. But the glowing colors, airy spaciousness, and free brushwork show his personal stylistic traits as they developed under Venetian influence. This sketch with its firmly modeled figures, is illustrative of the kind of spacious and buoyant compositions that Ricci took with him north of the Alps and established his international reputation.   D.M.

Lent by the Museum of Fine Arts, Springfield, Massachusetts

GIOVANNI BATTISTA PITTONI (1687–1767)

Born in Venice, Pittoni was first trained by his uncle, Francesco Pittoni, and then probably by Balestra. There is no evidence of his ever having left Venice. He painted altarpieces, mythological scenes, and small devotional pictures for French, German, Spanish and Russian as well as Italian patrons. He painted on canvas and occasionally on copper; only one fresco of his is known. He was an active member of the *Collegio dei Pittori*. In 1727 he was elected to the Accademia Clementina in Bologna, and in 1758 he succeeded Tiepolo as President of the Venetian Academy. Many of his pictures were engraved by Monaco, Berardi and Wagner.

39. *THE SACRIFICE OF ISAAC.* Oil on copper. 5⅛ x 7 inches (13 x 8 cm).

This unpublished oil sketch corresponds to a painting in the second chapel on the right in San Francesco della Vigna, Venice, to which it came a few years ago from the nearby Oratorio delle Sacre Stimmate (Pl. 39A). No references to the painting have yet been found, and since it does not quite fit into the decoration of the little oratory, the picture was probably a donation of a private owner.

The sketch is strikingly like the painting in composition but very different in technique. In spite of its small size, the sketch is painted in vigorous broad strokes that invest it with a monumentality different from the larger painting. Owing to the smooth finish of the final work, the high drama we see in the sketch, particularly noticeable in Abraham's awesome surprise, has lost its intensity and immediacy. But this difference in handling does not compel us to assume a different hand nor even a different date. Pittoni's oil sketches, especially those for his early paintings, show a vigor entirely lacking in their finished counterparts.

Despite the change of style, the compositions of sketch and final version are identical. The key to this consistency is provided by Pittoni's drawings, which painstakingly elaborate a composition until all problems of design and lighting are resolved in a last master drawing. The grand scale of these drawings and their meticulous, almost pedantic, finish would make a bozzetto superfluous were it not that the color still remained to be settled. This was the specific function of the oil sketch, for Pittoni left nothing to chance.

The present sketch together with the final painting can be dated by the composition, expressiveness, and iconography. A composition based on two or three vigorous and over-large figures seen against a uniform and empty background is rather rare in Pittoni's *œuvre*. In his historical paintings he always provides some kind of setting in which languid Rococo figures move decorously, elegantly, and undramatically. Here by contrast the emotion is violent; in another work by Pittoni, *The Martyrdom of Saint Thomas* in San Stae, Venice, datable in the late 1710's, we find an expressiveness so nearly identical that the two must have been painted at about the same time. The subject likewise suggests a date shortly before 1720, for around 1715 Federigo Bencovich painted a series of works, among them a *Sacrifice of Isaac,* which excited the rising generation of painters to adopt his technique as well as his highly dramatic Baroque imagery. Venice became obsessed with the subject of Abraham's sacrifice: numberless versions were painted at the time, some closely modeled on Bencovich's, such as Pittoni's, Migliori's and Damini's, others of greater inventiveness, such as Tiepolo's and Piazzetta's. Pittoni may conceivably have borrowed his composition from a later version of Bencovich's work. On the other hand, there is a compelling claim to assume Bencovich's direct influence in the few works by Pittoni which are moving rather than pleasing.   A.B.

Lent by Mr. and Mrs. Paul Ganz, New York

GIOVANNI ANTONIO PELLEGRINI (1675–1741)

Pellegrini was born and died in Venice, having spent most of his career outside of Italy. He was trained under Paolo Pagani, whom he may have accompanied to Austria before 1700, the year he went to Rome. In 1708 he went to England where he decorated Kimbolton Castle, Castle Howard, and other country houses. From 1713 to 1716 he worked in Düsseldorf, and the following years brought him to The Hague, to Paris (where he decorated the ceiling of the Banque de France), Vienna, Würzburg and Prague, with visits to Venice in between. He painted a few frescoes but worked mainly in large decorative panels on canvas.

40. *JEZEBEL INDUCING AHAB TO WORSHIP BAAL.* Oil on paper mounted on cardboard. 6 x 7¼ inches (15 x 18.5 cm). COLLECTION: Mestral de St. Saphorin. EXHIBITION: *Disegni e dipinti di Giovanni Antonio Pellegrini,* Venice, 1959, No. 110.

When exhibited for the first time in 1959, this sketch went under the title of "Solomon Worshipping the Idols" (Kings I:11). It represents, however, Jezebel inducing her husband, Ahab, to worship Baal (Kings I:16). The passage in the Book of Kings referring to Solomon's worship of idols speaks explicitly of the "old" king, while in the present sketch a youthful king is burning incense to the easily identifiable Baal at the injunction of an overpowering woman, clearly Jezebel. The sketch is executed in Pellegrini's very distinctive light palette. No painting of his connected with it has so far been traced, but an authorship other than his could hardly be argued.

On style alone, the present sketch can be assigned to his later period. In the sketches of his early maturity, as exemplified by those connected with his work at Bensberg Castle (1713–1716), his very broad and long zigzagging brushstrokes stand out distinctly; later, fluidity and blending set in and the reddish-brown still present in the early 1720's disappeared. The present sketch is most akin to the four overdoors in the Würzburg Residenz, designed in Paris and delivered early in 1737. For one pair the themes were biblical, and the present sketch is so close to them in the lighting and in the number, disposition, and relative sizes of the figures that it is tempting to regard it as a first, discarded suggestion for one of them.

A fair number of Pellegrini's oil sketches are known. Few can be dated, and those that can be linked to finished paintings are still fewer. As in the sketch shown here, Pellegrini's sketches convey the impression of having been executed in haste and with great intensity. He at once drew and painted with his brush, fixing both composition and lighting. Since the drawings that can be linked to finished paintings are of such puzzling scarcity (1 out of 107 at the exhibition of Pellegrini's drawings in Venice in 1959), one may tentatively conclude that in many cases the whole creative elaboration from first idea to finished product was condensed in the oil sketch. And since no more than a single sketch for any given painting has so far emerged, one may also suggest that Pellegrini combined bozzetto with modello in the one sketch whenever circumstances and patrons permitted. A.B.

Lent by Mr. Janos Scholz, New York

GIOVANNI BATTISTA PIAZZETTA (1683–1754)

Born in Venice, son of the sculptor Giacomo Piazzetta, Giovanni Battista entered the studio of the painter Antonio Molinari, perhaps after some training in sculpture at home. Later he studied in Bologna under Giuseppe Maria Crespi. In 1711 he returned to Venice, where he stayed until his death. He was an active member of the *Collegio dei Pittori,* was elected member of the Accademia Clementina of Bologna in 1727, and in 1750 became Director of the (still unofficial) Venetian Academy. He painted altarpieces, some genre scenes and one decorative ceiling on canvas. He won great fame for his drawings of heads and half-figures in black chalk. Many of his works were engraved and used in academies as teaching material.

41. *THE GUARDIAN ANGEL.* Oil on canvas. 26 x 18½ inches (67.2 x 47.4 cm).
EXHIBITIONS: *Christmas in Art,* Pomona College, California, 1952; *The Madonna in Art,* The Fine Arts Gallery, San Diego, 1957. LITERATURE: A. Morassi, "The Young Tiepolo," *Burlington Magazine,* LXVII, 1935, p. 144; R. Pallucchini, "Unbekannte Werke Piazzettas," *Pantheon,* XXIX, 1942, p. 49 ff.; W. Arslan, "Note breve sul Piazzetta," *Le Arti,* V, 1943, pp. 206–212; *Bulletin of the Art Division of the Los Angeles County Museum,* I, No. 1, 1947, p. 27; M. Brunetti, "Un eccezionale collegio peritale: Piazzetta, Tiepolo, Longhi," *Arte Veneta,* V, 1951, pp. 158–160.

The guardian angel on the left, looking up to the Virgin and Child, pleads for intercession on behalf of the souls in Purgatory, to which he points with his left hand. His right hand reaches over a child running to him for protection. On the lower right a soul is struggling to get out of the pit. On the right, close to the Virgin, is a soul just released from Purgatory. This small sketch, hitherto referred to as *The Madonna of Protection,* should be called *The Guardian Angel,* as it so perfectly illustrates the guardian angel's double function: to protect man during his journey on earth—especially in childhood, when protection is most needed—and to comfort him after death, if need be in Purgatory, while interceding for his release.

The large painting with which the present sketch is connected no longer exists in its entirety. Only a relatively large fragment survives, roughly the upper-right section of the composition (now in the Museum of Fine Arts in Detroit). The first reference to the painting as a work by Piazzetta appears in an inventory of the paintings in the palazzo of the Venetian nobleman Gherardo Sagredo, made at his death in 1738. This inventory was drawn up by Tiepolo and Piazzetta himself— painters were not infrequently called upon to make inventories—and the painting, called *Angelo Custode (Guardian Angel),* was evaluated at 400 ducats, an impressive sum at the time. The Kassel Gallery (Germany) has a small version of the same subject by Piazzetta that is strikingly close to the Los Angeles sketch exhibited here. It is of similar size but somewhat different shape, the top being slightly rounded. Formerly some scholars attributed the two sketches and the Detroit fragment to Tiepolo and dated them into the early 1720's. The misattribution is excusable in view of the closeness of Tiepolo's to Piazzetta's pictorial language of about 1720. This closeness obtains between *The Guardian Angel* and Tiepolo's *Madonna del Carmelo* of 1720–22

(Brera, Milan) : the head of the Virgin in each work seems even to derive from the same model. But the discovery by Arslan of an engraving of *The Guardian Angel* after Piazzetta and the publication of the Sagredo inventory settled the question of attribution once and for all. As for the date, the inventory of 1738 provides an *ante quem,* but the work belongs to a much earlier phase of Piazzetta's stylistic development. The present sketch recalls Piazzetta's drastic chiaroscuro of the period before 1720, in which light and shadow coexist without interpenetrating, but the passage from light to dark is already softened. And while in earlier works the figures loom bulky and even are crowded at times in a space too small for them, they appear here in their entirety, with voids of space between them. In composition and execution *The Guardian Angel* marks a transition in Piazzetta's development. On both counts the picture was apparently precursory to his great masterpiece of 1725, *The Madonna Appearing to Saint Philip Neri,* in the Fava Church in Venice.

In current literature the Los Angeles sketch is generally called a bozzetto, a preliminary sketch made by the artist for himself, while the small painting in Kassel is referred to as a modello, the small version of a prospective painting submitted to the customer for approbation. The two appellations are convenient, but nonetheless arbitrary. The Kassel version does convey more, but only slightly more, 'finish,' and the composition in both is not quite identical. The postures of the two putti in the upper left differ; moreover, they are far more harmoniously integrated in the present version than in the Kassel one, where they dangle somewhat awkwardly, suggesting an assistant's hand. The engraving made after the large painting is identical with the Los Angeles piece —putti and all—so that the so-called bozzetto may well be a modello after all, and the small painting in Kassel may well have been executed later as a devotional picture. The fact that it has a pendant (also in Kassel) argues strongly in this direction since pendants to bozzetti or modelli are rare indeed.   A.B.

Lent by the Los Angeles County Museum of Art, Gift of Adolph Loewi

GIOVANNI BATTISTA TIEPOLO (1696–1770)

Born in Venice, Tiepolo studied under Gregorio Lazzarini, but was on the lists of the Venetian Guild of Painters as an independent master as early as 1717. Though he painted many easel pictures and made etchings, his preferred medium was the fresco, and he decorated many palaces and churches in Venice and in other North Italian cities. Invited to Würzburg in 1750, he worked there until 1753 with his sons Giovanni Domenico and Lorenzo on the decoration of the *Kaisersaal* and the *Residenz*. In 1762 Charles III called him to Spain, where he worked in the Royal Palace at Madrid and where he remained until his death.

42. *THE TEMPTATION OF SAINT ANTHONY.* Oil on canvas. 15¾ x 18½ inches (40 x 47 cm). COLLECTION: M. Lederer, Vienna. EXHIBITION: *Mostra del Tiepolo,* Venice, 1951, No. 19; *Mostra della pittura veneta del settecento in Friuli,* Udine, 1966, No. 74. LITERATURE: E. Modigliani, "Dipinti noti e malnoti di Giambattista Tiepolo," *Dedalo,* XIII, 1933, pp. 133 ff; A. Morassi, *A Complete Catalogue of the Paintings of G. B. Tiepolo,* London, 1962, p. 24.

We see here a bold new treatment of an old pictorial theme: the temptation of Saint Anthony. A remarkably expressive, half-prostrate Saint Anthony recoils from the glaring vision of the temptress. Weakened by his inward struggle, he raises his book in a somewhat helpless gesture, as if to erect a barrier between his world and hers. She, a placid, statuesque nude, inclines her head to listen to the devil's instructions. The two worlds meet within a mysterious setting overcast by a livid, spectral light and rendered the more fantastic by the chromatic discordance between the temptress's rosy flesh and the monk's dark cowl. The hallucinatory quality of the scene is intensified through the juxtaposition of the trees against the sky and the clouds down on the earth, a commingling of the real and the unreal.

This exquisite sketch is an early work by Tiepolo and can be grouped with several others in the same vein executed around 1725. Of these, *The Penitent Magdalen* (Achille Lamo Collection, Naples) and *Saint Louis Gonzaga* (Count Seilern Collection, London) are perhaps the most akin to the *The Temptation of Saint Anthony*: in all are found the same incandescent lighting and heavy woolly clouds.

At this time Tiepolo was approaching the most important turning point in his stylistic development. He was soon to abandon his sombre dramatic manner, derived from Piazzetta and Bencovich, and to invest his works with festive radiant colors. This sketch still belongs to his early manner, though it foreshadows his mature style in the easing of the patches of light and of the sombre background. The three trees are new in Tiepolo's work and prefigure the idyllic settings he was to depict a year or two later in his masterly Udine frescoes.

Throughout his career Tiepolo always set down a complete composition in his preparatory oil sketches and modelli. With the exception of some large-sized modelli the technique was broad and undetailed. In view of the careful structure of the body of the seductress and of such details as the tree leaves, we may wonder if the present sketch is not a work in its own right, but we cannot yet provide a final answer.

A.B.

Lent by the Pinacoteca di Brera, Milan

43. *SKETCH FOR THE CEILING OF AENEAS IN THE ROYAL PALACE, MADRID.* Oil on canvas. 27½ x 19¼ inches (68.8 x 48.8 cm). COLLECTIONS: Baron Herzog, Budapest; Marcel von Nemes, Munich; Charles Fairfax Murray, London; Joseph Spiridon (?), Paris; de Beurnonville, Paris. EXHIBITION: *Mostra del Tiepolo,* Venice, 1951, No. 97. LITERATURE: J. C. Bermudez, "Tiepolo," in *Diccionario de Ilustres Profesores de las Bellas Artes en España,* Madrid, 1800; F. J. Fabre, *Descripcion de las alegorías pintadas en las bovedas del Real Palacio de Madrid,* Madrid, 1829; P. Molmenti, *G. B. Tiepolo,* Milano, 1909, pp. 185–186; E. Sack, *Giambattista und Domenico Tiepolo,* Hamburg, 1910, pp. 137–138; S. de Vito Battaglia, *Il bozzetto di Giambattista Tiepolo per il soffito della Sala de la Guardia nel Palazzo Reale di Madrid,* Rome, 1931; G. Fiocco, "Giambattista Tiepolo in Spagna," *Nuova Antologia,* No. 390, 1937, pp. 329–334; A. Morassi, *A Complete Catalogue of the Paintings of G. B. Tiepolo,* London, 1962, p. 57; J. Rosenberg, "An Oil Sketch by G. B. Tiepolo for the Aeneas Ceiling in Madrid," *Bulletin of the Fogg Art Museum,* XI, 1950, pp. 53–61; F. J. Sanchez Canton, *J. B. Tiepolo en España,* Madrid, 1953.

In April of 1762, Tiepolo, accompanied by his sons Giandomenico and Lorenzo, left Venice for Madrid where he was to decorate rooms in the newly-built Royal Palace. There, between 1762 and 1766, he painted three ceilings, and the present sketch is connected with that in the hall of the Royal Guard, probably painted in 1766, the last of the series. The ceiling has gone under various names by reason of its complex iconography, combining two separate passages from the *Aeneid* (I,

259–264 and VIII, 606–630). The first tells of Jupiter's promise to Venus that one day her son Aeneas will be immortalized and that she will see him rise to heaven. The second tells how, when Aeneas was fighting the Latin tribes, Venus had Vulcan forge arms for him, then descended to earth to surprise him with her gifts. Tiepolo told this double story in his own free way, yet faithfully. On the lower left is Vulcan's forge and the half-reclining god directs the Cyclops to make the arms. On the lower right, Aeneas' comrades, led by Achates, rush forth ready for battle. Chronos, seated on a rock, holds part of the new armor in his right hand. Aeneas, standing on a cloud supported by putti, extends his hand to receive from Venus the helmet forged by Vulcan; he has already received the sword. So much for the second episode. As for the first, the hero is surrounded by allegorical figures: winged Victory with her palm, laurel-crowned Merit with his lion, and what may be Fortitude. Venus and two Graces watch Aeneas ascend to the temple of immortality; Aeneas is placed higher than Chronos, who has no more power over him. This dual subject of a great warrior receiving arms before going to battle and his reward after victory was most appropriate to a hall for soldiers.

A similar sketch connected with the same ceiling is in the Boston Museum. It is by the same hand (and not by Domenico's, as has been conjectured) but corresponds to an earlier stage in the elaboration of the composition. It already contains all the figures, but the relationship between the groups is not yet so lucid and clear as in the present sketch, which was probably the last one made as it shows the final composition. But the necessity of stretching it out on the large ceiling somewhat impaired the beautiful balance between the figures and the cloudy voids: on the ceiling the figures look a little lost in their vast heavens.

A.B.

Lent by the Fogg Art Museum, Harvard University, Allston Burr Fund

44. *NEPTUNE AND THE WINDS*. Oil on canvas. 24½ x 24½ inches (62.2 x 62.2 cm). COLLECTIONS: Madrazo, Madrid; Gimpel and Wildenstein, Paris, 1912; Marquis de Biron, Paris and Geneva, 1912–1937. EXHIBITION: *Tiepolo and his Contemporaries*, Metropolitan Museum of Art, New York, 1938, No. 13. LITERATURE: G. Knox, *Catalogue of the Tiepolo Drawings in the Victoria and Albert*

Museum, London, 1960, pp. 91–92; A. Morassi, *A Complete Catalogue of the Paintings of G. B. Tiepolo,* London, 1962, p. 33, fig. 255.

In front of a round temple in a mist of clouds sits Jupiter beside a reclining goddess (Juno or perhaps Venus). On the lower left Neptune, trident in hand, bids the winds in the central foreground to calm. Although the floating figure on the left cannot be identified, the subject is most likely related to the passage of the *Aeneid* in which Neptune halts the winds sent by Juno to shipwreck Aeneas' fleet (I, 124 ff).

This sketch by Tiepolo has not yet been linked to any known painting, but is obviously a preparation for a circular ceiling decoration. The meticulously elaborated, beautifully composed Neptune group contrasts with the looser forms of the rest. Since Tiepolo otherwise worked out his preparatory oil studies in every particular, this one may even represent a conception abandoned midway. On style alone it fits best in Tiepolo's late Spanish period, 1762–1770. A near replica of the figure of Neptune is found on Tiepolo's ceiling of the Throne Room in the Royal Palace of Madrid, and a drawing, undoubtedly from Tiepolo's late Spanish period, contains figure studies closely related to both Neptunes. The subject of Tiepolo's ceiling in the hall of the Royal Guard in the palace, for which a sketch is on view here (No. 43), is also taken from the story of Aeneas. But the present sketch cannot possibly be a discarded first idea for it because that ceiling could not have accommodated a circular decoration.

Tiepolo's Spanish period is considered by some to have been the climax, by others the decline, of his art. His figures of this period are drawn from a seasoned repertory, for example the winds here, which duplicate those painted by him on a ceiling of the Villa Valmarana (in the Iphigenia room). But if the particulars carry over from the past, the compositions—as is exemplified by the Neptune group in the present sketch—evidence an inventiveness unimpaired up to the last. A.B.

Lent by the Metropolitan Museum of Art, New York, Rogers Fund, 1937

GIOVANNI ANTONIO CANAL, called CANALETTO
(1697–1768)

Son of the stage designer Bernardo Canal, Giovanni Antonio was born in Venice on October 28, 1697. He received his early training from his father, with whom he collaborated until approximately 1719. In that year he visited Rome. Though he was influenced by Carlevaris, no evidence of his having been Carlevaris' pupil is known. In 1720 his name appeared for the first time in the books of the Venetian Guild of Painters. He seems never to have married, but he fostered and trained his nephew Bernardo Bellotto, who became an artist of repute. Canaletto is mainly known for his views of Venice, but he also painted *capricci* and made etchings. He was patronized by the English consul in Venice, Joseph Smith, who amassed the largest collection of his views. From 1746 to 1756 he lived in England except for two trips back to Venice. In 1763 he was elected to the Venetian Academy. He died in Venice on April 19, 1768.

45. *FIGURE STUDIES*. Oil on paper laid down on board. 15⅞ x 23 inches (40.3 x 58.4 cm). Inscription on reverse in 19th century hand: *Canaletti's original sketches for the pictures belonging to her Majesty, now in the corridor of Windsor Castle*. COLLECTIONS: John Samuel, Park Lane; Miss Lucy Cohen; Hon. Neil Primrose; Countess of Halifax. EXHIBITIONS: *Works of Art*, Leeds, 1868; *Life in Eighteenth Century Venice*, The Iveagh Bequest, Kenwood, Greater London Council, 1966. LITERATURE: W. G. Constable, "Canaletto as a Figure Painter," *Apollo*, LXXIX, 1964, pp. 108–113.

The sketch is one of a series of three studies in oil, with figures, that emerged from oblivion a few years ago. The figures are of no precise time or place except that they wear clothes and wigs of the mid-18th century. The three oil sketches were attributed to Carlevaris when they were discovered and to Canaletto after they had been cleaned. Analysis has established that they must have been painted at about the same time. The 19th-century inscription on the back states that the figures in the sketch appear in paintings by Canaletto now in the Royal Collection at Windsor; in fact they recur in five different paintings of two different series: a Venetian series of views evidently painted between 1726 and 1728 and a Roman series signed and dated 1742. W. G. Constable, who studied the sketches carefully, has come to the conclusion that Canaletto painted them while working on the Venetian views, that he utilized some of the figures then and kept the rest as studio material for other occasions. But one may wonder how Canaletto, who seems never to have repeated figures in his paintings, could have remembered through the years which of the figures in these sketches he had used and which he had not. In the sketch here exhibited the light falls on the figures from different angles, exactly as on their counterparts in the paintings at Windsor. If then they are preparatory studies, Canaletto would have had to foresee the angles at which the light was to fall in each of those views he was to paint fifteen years later. One is tempted to assume that despite their sketchy character the figures were made from the paintings rather than for them. If this conclusion were correct, our sketch and the two others mentioned above could not have been executed in Canaletto's studio, since the two series of paintings were probably not there together at any time. Both series belonged to Joseph Smith's collection, which was sold to George III of England in 1763–1764; thus both must have hung in Consul Smith's palazzo until then, visible and accessible to all, including Canaletto himself.

Now it is most striking that the figure studies of our sketch look as if they were made from life; they are loose, fresh, and painted with a rapid brush in contrast to the static and firm quality of the figures in the Roman series but in conformity with those in the Venetian set of pictures. This strongly suggests that the author of the sketch was after all the author of the Venetian set, Canaletto, but also that the Roman series, though signed by Canaletto, was primarily the workshop production by an assistant, presumably Bellotto, whose style the set strikingly recalls. An enigma remains: no other oil sketches of this kind by Canaletto have come down to us.   A.B.

Lent Anonymously

GIOVANNI ANTONIO GUARDI (1699–1760)

Born in Vienna, Giovanni Antonio Guardi may have received his early training in Venice from his father, Domenico. After Domenico's death in 1716, Gianantonio went to Vienna, where he was close to Giuseppe Galli-Bibiena. Back in Venice, he painted altarpieces, devotional pictures, battle scenes, and mythological and historical subjects. Although he was the head of the family workshop, his younger brother

Francesco, the famous painter of *vedute,* has until recently been credited as the only genius in the studio. Four years before his death Gianantonio was one of the founding members of the Venetian Academy.

46. *ATHENA DICTATING LAWS TO ODYSSEUS* (?). Oil on canvas. 13¾ x 15¾ inches (35 x 40 cm). COLLECTION: Lavalard. EXHIBITION: *Tiepolo et Guardi dans les collections françaises,* Paris, Galerie Cailleux, 1952, No. 118. LITERATURE: Cat. Lavalard, 1899, No. 237; E. Sack, *Giambattista und Domenico Tiepolo,* Hamburg, 1910; W. Arslan, "Appunti su Magnasco, Sebastiano e Marco Ricci," *Bolletino d'Arte,* XXVI, 1932, p. 211; E. Arslan, "Per la definizione dell'arte di Francesco, Giannantonio e Nicolò Guardi," *Emporium,* C, 1944, pp. 3–28.

This sketch long passed for a work by Tiepolo, whose authorship was first questioned by Sack in 1910. Arslan attributed it to Francesco Guardi in 1932, then some years later to Gianantonio. The disentanglement of the Guardi brothers has for some decades been a source of scholarly contention and strife. But by now Gianantonio's artistic personality has emerged more clearly and the present sketch seems typical of him.

Its composition is a faithful copy of an etching by G. B. Tiepolo, one of the *capricci* published by Zanetti between 1739 and 1743. The possibility that the ever-inventive Tiepolo should have appropriated a composition by Gianantonio can safely be discarded. In contrast, Gianantonio, who started his career as a copyist, was an inveterate borrower, taking unrestrainedly from masters old and new, great and small, domestic and foreign. Yet the present sketch is the first known instance of his having borrowed from his wealthy brother-in-law.

The iconography is puzzling. Tiepolo's *capriccio* is entitled *Young Soldier and Astrologer* in the catalogue of his etchings prepared after his death by his son. In the Museum at Amiens, the Guardi sketch is called *Athena Dictating Laws to Odysseus.* The central figure is indeed decked out as Athena; Homer's Odysseus, however, did not write.

This work is the smallest known painting by Gianantonio, except for some early devotional pictures of uncertain attribution, and the only one to have been widely called a bozzetto, probably because of its technique and small format. But no painting connected with it is known, just as no preparatory sketches are known for his larger paintings. The extreme bravura of the brush-stroke would signal a sketch were it not that the finished works of Gianantonio's maturity are painted in this very manner in which line and contour are transcended. Dabs of pigment create but do not bind the particular forms, which thus melt into the surrounding atmosphere. In this sketch, the three heads and the helmet are prodigies of such impressionistic painting and relate the work in style to the series painted on the organ parapet of the church of the Angelo Raffaele in Venice, assigned to Gianantonio's late maturity and accepted as ranking with the loftiest creations of the Venetian Rococo.

Since Gianantonio copied this composition, he cannot have intended it as a preparatory work. And since this sketch is a copy after Tiepolo, it cannot have served as a modello for a patron. We may have here simply a study sketch in its own right, made by Gianantonio for his own purposes.   A.B.

Lent by the Musée de Picardie, Amiens

The Low Countries

PETER PAUL RUBENS (1577–1640)

Before he left for Italy in 1600, Rubens was trained in Antwerp under Tobias Verhaecht, Adam van Noort, and Otto van Veen. In Italy he obtained important commissions in Genoa and Rome and worked in Mantua for Duke Vincenzo Gonzaga, for whom he made a trip to Spain in 1603. Back in Antwerp in 1608, Rubens made his home there and began a painting career that brought him international fame and honor. Aside from altarpieces, portraits, mythological and allegorical subjects handled in single pictures, Rubens was also responsible for such large cycles as the decoration of the Jesuit church in Antwerp, the *Life of Maria de' Medici* for the Palais du Luxembourg in Paris, the ceiling of the Banqueting House in Whitehall, London, and the hunting lodge of Philip IV, the Torre de la Parada, outside Madrid. A successful diplomat as well as painter, Rubens was knighted by both Philip IV and Charles I.

47. *ST. GREGORY OF NAZIANZUS.* Oil on panel. 19¾ x 25¾ inches (50.2 x 65.4 cm). COLLECTIONS: M. de Burtin, Brussels; Duke Ernest II of Gotha, 1801; Gotha Museum until 1951; E. and A. Silberman Galleries, New York, 1952. EXHIBITIONS: *L'art belge au XVIIe siècle*, Brussels, 1910 (see *Trésor de l'art belge au XVIIe siècle*, I, 1912, No. XV); *Esquisses de Rubens*, Musées Royaux des Beaux-Arts de Belgique, Brussels, 1937, No. 68; *Olieverfschetsen van Rubens*, Museum Boymans, Rotterdam, 1953, No. 27; E. and A. Silberman Galleries, New York, 1955, No. 18; *Drawings and Oil Sketches of Peter Paul Rubens*, Fogg Art Museum, Cambridge, Mass., 1956, No. 31; *Trends in Painting, 1600–1800*, Albright-Knox Art Gallery, Buffalo, New York, 1957, p. 12; *Paintings and Sculpture from the Albright Art Gallery*, Yale University Art Gallery, New Haven, Conn., 1961, No. 70; *Le siècle de Rubens*, Musées Royaux des Beaux-Arts de Belgique, Brussels, 1965, No. 221. LITERATURE: J. Smith, *Catalogue raisonné*, London, 1830, II, p. 17; *Catalog der herzoglichen Gemäldegalerie*, Gotha, 1858, pt. LV, No. 481 (1890, No. 36); M. Rooses, *L'oeuvre de Rubens*, Antwerp, 1886, I, No. 25 bis (contract on pp. 43–45); R. Oldenbourg, *P. P. Rubens: des Meisters Gemälde* (Klassiker der Kunst, V), 4th ed., *Stuttgart*, 1921, p. 207; L. van Puyvelde, *The Sketches of Rubens*, London, 1947, p. 27; M. Jaffé, "Addition to the Permanent Collection: The Sketch of St. Gregory Nazianzenus by Rubens," *Buffalo Fine Arts Academy: Gallery Notes*, XVII, Nos. 2 and 3, 1953, pp. 2–6; J. S. Held, "A Postscript: Rubens in America," *Art Digest*, XXVIII, No. 16, 1954, pp. 13, 35; J. S. Held, *Rubens: Selected Drawings*, London, 1959, p. 113, under No. 47.

Lent by the Albright-Knox Art Gallery, Buffalo, New York

48. *ELIJAH.* Oil on panel. 12¾ x 17¾ inches (32.5 x 44 cm). COLLECTIONS: An oil sketch of this subject was listed in the inventory of Herman Neyt, Antwerp, 1642, No. 747 (according to the Rotterdam Catalogue, 1953); M. de Burtin, Brussels; Duke Ernest II of Gotha, 1801; Gotha Museum until 1951; E. and A. Silberman Galleries, New York, 1952. EXHIBITIONS: *L'art belge au XVIIe siècle*, Brussels, 1910 (see *Trésor de l'art belge au XVIIe siècle*, I, 1912, No. XV); *Esquisses de Rubens*, Musées Royaux des Beaux-Arts de Belgique, Brussels, 1937, No. 66; *Olieverfschetsen van Rubens*, Museum Boymans, Rotterdam, 1953, No. 30; *Drawings and Oil Sketches of Peter Paul Rubens*, Fogg Art Museum, Cambridge, Mass., 1956, No. 30; *Art United Nations*, E. and A. Silberman Galleries, New York, 1957, No. 11; *Le siècle de Rubens*, Musées Royaux des Beaux-Arts de Belgique, Brussels, 1965, No. 220. LITERATURE: J. Smith, *Catalogue raisonné*, London, 1830, II, p. 17, No. 46; M. Rooses, *L'oeuvre de Rubens*, Antwerp, 1886, I, No. 15 bis; *Catalog der herzoglichen Gemäldegalerie*, Gotha, 1910, No. 38; R. Oldenbourg, *P. P. Rubens: des Meisters Gemälde* (Klassiker der Kunst, V), 4th ed., Stuttgart, 1921, p. 210; L. van Puyvelde, *The Sketches of Rubens*, London, 1947, p. 28; M. Jaffé, "Rubens Sketching in Paint," *Art News*, LII, May 1953, pp. 34 ff.

Lent by Mr. George Baer, New York

These sketches were made in connection with Rubens' decorations for the St. Carolus Borromaeus-Kerk, the new Jesuit church in Antwerp. Destroyed by fire on July 18, 1718, the paintings are known from wash drawing copies made by de Witt and Müller, engravings made by Punt and Preisler, and the numerous extant oil sketches by Rubens' own hand (*KdK*, pp. 207–215). According to the contract of March 29, 1620, Rubens was to provide 39 panels for the ceiling compartments of the nave and side aisles, representing scenes from the New Testament placed next to those subjects from the Old Testament which prefigured them. In order to complete the commission, promised for the end of the year, Rubens was allowed to use assistants in the execution, but he was to provide all the oil sketches. In addition he was to execute an altarpiece by his own hand for one of the side chapels or else give all the ceiling sketches to the Father Superior.

St. Gregory of Nazianzus was sixth in the list of 34 subjects actually specified in the contract. In the sketch the saint is shown robed in a gray mantle, standing on a bank of clouds. With an angelic putto who holds a veil flying above him and with his crozier in hand, St. Gregory forcefully repulses Heresy, a fantastic figure with a human body, tiger's head and claws of an eagle. Rubens took into account the oblique angle from which the scene would be viewed by a spectator below and adjusted the figures dramatically to this foreshortened viewpoint.

The sketches, typical of those surviving for this project, have a triple function: to clarify his original thoughts previously worked out in drawings; to show the final stage to the Jesuits for their approval; and to give his assistants the detailed models to follow in the execution. Of the drawings for the Jesuit church, only one for the *St. Gregory* has survived, a chalk drawing now in New York (Clarence L. Hay Collection; Held, *Selected Drawings*, No. 47, pl. 49). The oil sketch is based on the drawing but simplifies the composition in such a way that the full drama of conflict emerges more powerfully. In the final version, as we know from the copies, Rubens made a few minor changes to strengthen the meaning of the image. The figure of Heresy, for example, was more humanized and the putto was also shown pushing the crozier, reinforcing its thrust.

Twenty-fifth on the list attached to the contract, the *Elijah* dramatically illustrates the verse from the Old Testament, Second Kings, II, 11: "And it came to pass . . . that behold, there appeared a chariot of fire, and horses of fire . . . and Elijah went up by a whirlwind into heaven." Rubens has given true life to these words, and we see Elijah, his eyes burning, turning back to look down at the spectator as his chariot is swept by two horses across a flaming sky. The intensity of expression of this superb sketch is of course lost in Jan Punt's engraving (Rooses, I, pl. 8, IV), but it does show that one of the two horses was apparently eliminated in the executed picture. The energy and dynamic force of the Elijah as we see him in the sketch are so great that we can hardly imagine that they could be improved, but perhaps Rubens thought that two horses diffused Elijah's own specific power and so finally decided to give him only one.   S.B.S.

49. *PEACE EMBRACING PLENTY.* Oil on panel. 23¾ x 18½ inches (60.3 x 47 cm). COLLECTIONS: King Charles I of England; M. Davoust (sale, 1772); Trouard sale, Paris, February 22, 1779, No. 93 (bought by de Cossé); sale, Paris, December 11, 1780, No. 35; J. B. Horion, Brussels, 1781; Horion sale, 1788; Sir Joshua Reynolds sale, London, 1795; Matthew Mitchell sale, Enfield, 1819; Pinney; H. Baillie, 1830; Dawson Turner, Yarmouth, by 1840, purchased from Mr. Philip Pauné; Kleinberger, Paris, 1911; Dowdeswell, London; Leopold Koppel, Berlin; Paul Klotz, Pontresina. EXHIBITIONS: So-called "Orleans Gallery" Exhibition, London, 1873, No. 152; *Paintings by Old Masters,* Kleinberger Galleries, New York, 1911, No. 93; *Esquisses de Rubens,* Musées Royaux des Beaux-Arts de Belgique, Brussels, 1937, No. 98; *Masterpieces of Art,* New York World's Fair, 1939, No. 336; *Masterpieces of Art,* Detroit Institute of Arts, 1939, No. 43; *Seven Centuries of Paintings,* N. H. de Young Memorial Museum, San Francisco, 1939–40, No. Y 45; *Masterpieces of Art,* Carnegie Institute, Pittsburgh, 1940, No. 18; *Masterpieces of Art,* City Art Museum, St. Louis, 1940; *Loan Exhibition of Rubens and Van Dyck,* Los Angeles County Museum, 1946, No. 35; *A Loan Exhibition of Rubens,* Wildenstein, New York, 1951, No. 26; *Le siècle de Rubens,* Musées Royaux des Beaux-Arts de Belgique, Brussels, 1965, No. 230. LITERATURE: J. Smith, *Catalogue raisonné,* London, 1830, II, p. 199, No. 717; M. Rooses, *L'oeuvre de Rubens,* Antwerp, 1890, III, No. 766; R. Oldenbourg, *P. P. Rubens: des Meisters Gemälde* (Klassiker der Kunst, V), 4th ed., Stuttgart, 1921, p. 336; L. van Puyvelde, *The Sketches of Rubens,* London, 1947, p. 39. A pen drawing of this subject, formerly in the Fairfax Murray Collection, is in the Institut Néerlandais, F. Lugt Collection. (For the Whitehall ceiling, see: O. Millar, "The Whitehall Ceiling," *Burlington Magazine,* XCVIII, 1956, pp. 258–267; P. Palme, *Triumph of Peace: A Study of the Whitehall Banqueting House,* London, 1957; O. Millar, *Rubens: The Whitehall Ceiling,* London, 1958; J. Charlton, *The Banqueting House, Whitehall,* London, 1964 [reproductions in color].)

During the early 1630's Rubens was occupied with a commission, entrusted to him by Charles I of England, to decorate the ceiling of the new Banqueting House in Whitehall with an *Apotheosis of James I*. The old Banqueting House had been destroyed by fire on December 12, 1619, and by 1621 Inigo Jones had completed the new building. He divided its ceiling into nine compartments long before Rubens began painting. Rubens probably obtained the commission during his trip to London in 1629, although as early as 1621 he had expressed a desire to serve James I at the "New Palace" (*The Letters of Peter Paul Rubens*, ed. R. Magurn, Cambridge, Mass., 1955, p. 77). Most of the work, however, was done after Rubens' return to Antwerp in 1630. For the large central oval panel he designed the *Apotheosis of James I* and for the rectangular spaces at either end the *Union of the Crowns of England and Scotland* and the *Benefits of the Government of James I*. In addition, he depicted allegories for the four small, elongated ovals at the corners of the ceiling and two friezes of putti for the long, narrow rectangles on either side of the *Apotheosis*. The canvases were executed in Rubens' workshop in Brussels and sent to England in 1635. The ceiling has been restored several times, most recently between 1947 and 1950, when its original aspect was to a large extent reclaimed; and though its condition is not entirely satisfactory, the ceiling remains unique in being the only one of Rubens' great cycles still in its original setting.

In the sketch shown here we see Peace, dressed in brilliant gold, leaning forward to clasp Plenty clad in a rose-colored robe and with a cornucopia on her lap: the scene clearly paraphrases the passage "righteousness and peace have kissed each other" in the 85th Psalm, a passage often illustrated in similar terms. Our sketch is only a detail of the larger scene that glorifies the benefits of James I's government. Rubens prepared the Whitehall ceiling with his usual care; for the scene under discussion he probably began with a rapid oil sketch of the entire composition. This assumption finds support in the aspect of our sketch which shows both figures and serpentine columns foreshortened for the beholder's viewpoint under the ceiling, a compositional device surely first clarified in a general study. The sketch before us is concerned with the clarification of details; it presents an image of ease and grace, a composition harmoniously satisfying and even visually complete. Rubens probably developed other details in oil sketches, but aside from ours only one such sketch is known, a detail for the *Wisdom Triumphing over War and Discord,* now in Brussels. Oil studies of parts of the composition were then absorbed into a fairly finished modello, and in our case the modello of the *Benefits of the Government of James I* has survived (in Vienna; *KdK,* p. 335). In it Rubens retained the architecture seen in the sketch, but shifted Peace and Plenty to the left and placed James I in front of the niche previously occupied by the allegories. The executed canvas follows the Vienna modello: in the translation into the full rhetoric of the completed allegory, our sketch not only changed its form but also lost its warmth and intimacy.

S.B.S.

Lent Anonymously   Frontispiece

50. *MEETING OF THE TWO FERDINANDS.* Oil on panel. 19 x 24¾ inches (48.3 x 62.9 cm). COLLECTIONS: Sir Abraham Hume, Bart.; Lord Brownlow (sale, London, May 4, 1923); Martin Sternberg; sale, Amsterdam, Fred. Muller Catalogue, October 25, 1932, No. 513. EXHIBITIONS: *Exposition Rubens,* Galerie Goudstikker, Amsterdam, 1933, No. 40; *Esquisses de Rubens,* Musées Royaux des Beaux-Arts de Belgique, Brussels, 1937, No. 90; *Meesterwerken uit vier Eeuwen 1400–1800,* Museum Boymans, Rotterdam, 1938, No. 179; Schaeffer Gallery, New York, 1942, No. 24; Wildenstein, New York, 1951, No. 29; *Olieverfschetsen van Rubens,* Museum Boymans, Rotterdam, 1953, No. 95; Museum of Art, Baltimore, 1954; *Drawings and Oil Sketches of Peter Paul Rubens,* Fogg Art Museum, Cambridge, Mass., 1956, No. 44. LITERATURE: J. Smith, *Catalogue raisonné,* London, 1830, II, p. 90 (mentions a chalk study for one of the females in Sir Thomas Lawrence's collection); M. Rooses, *L'oeuvre de Rubens,* Antwerp, 1890, III, No. 775; R. Oldenbourg, *P. P. Rubens: des Meisters Gemälde* (Klassiker der Kunst, V), 4th ed., Stuttgart, 1921, p. 363; H. G. Evers, *Peter Paul Rubens,* Munich, 1942, p. 368; L. van Puyvelde, *The Sketches of Rubens,* London, 1947, p. 40; J. Goris and J. S. Held, *Rubens in America,* New York, 1947, No. 88; M. Jaffé, "Rubens Sketching in Paint," *Art News,* LII, May 1953, p. 65.

In April of 1635 Cardinal-Infante Ferdinand of Spain, brother of Philip IV and new governor of Flanders, made his triumphal entry into Antwerp. The city of Antwerp celebrated the event by constructing a number of stages and triumphal arches decorated with scenes from Ferdinand's life. Rubens provided the designs for these decorations, which were executed by his assistants. The sketch showing the *Meeting of the Two Ferdinands* was designed for a large Stage of Welcome.

The central canvas of this stage showed the prince's arrival. To the left was the *Voyage of Cardinal-Infante Ferdinand from Spain to Italy* (Dresden: *KdK,* p. 362, oil sketch in the Fogg Art Museum, Cambridge), showing Neptune calming the seas so that the prince's fleet could safely make the voyage from Barcelona to Genoa. The *Meeting of the Two Ferdinands* was on the right (Vienna; *KdK,* p. 363). The latter showed Ferdinand of Spain joining forces with his cousin Ferdinand of Hungary in order to conquer Germany's Protestant armies. (The battle took place on September 2, 1634, at Nördlingen on the Danube.)

Our sketch shows a characteristic device of Rubens' late style, the separation of the historical event from the allegorical. To the right is the Cardinal-Infante of Spain stepping forward to greet his cousin; their followers stand behind them. Well in front of them are placed the personifications: Germania, dressed in black, kneels and gazes out as a putto urges her to look at the event, and at the left the Danube, with a nymph beside him, motions toward the portentous meeting. In the final picture Rubens made additional changes: he aligned, for example, the heads of the figures in the foreground so that these personifications no longer block any parts of the background scene. The distinction between allegory and history is thus made clearer, but the principle is already apparent in the sketch.

Rubens received the commission in November of 1634, and Ferdinand was scheduled to arrive the following January (although in fact the entry was postponed until April). Thus Rubens had to work rather quickly, without time for leisurely re-study. As he did in some other sketches, he here drew directly on the panel in black chalk, marks of which—for example in the sky on the left and near the margins on either side—are still visible where they were covered by only the varnish. The sketch gives us an opportunity to observe the full power of Rubens' mind and hand and of his genius in rapidly developing clear ideas in a cogent and dramatic way.   S.B.S.

Lent by Dr. Sonja Binkhorst-Kramarsky, New York

JACOB JORDAENS (1593–1678)

Jordaens was born in Antwerp, where he received his early training as a painter in tempera. He was apprenticed in 1607 to Adam van Noort, but as with Rubens, van Noort's other famous pupil, no influence of teacher upon pupil can be detected. In the years before 1620 his style came close to that of van Dyck, and his early work shows the impact of the realism and strong modeling of Caravaggio and, above all, of the style of Rubens. As Jordaens' style developed, the influence of Rubens declined, and in the 1650's Jordaens was strongly affected by the new Baroque Classicism that, under French influence, was sweeping the Lowlands. After Rubens' death in 1640, Jordaens became the most important and popular painter in Belgium, with a large and active studio. Toward the end of his life he joined a Calvinist community and his style grew more severe and ascetic. His early biblical and mythological subjects, feasts, and proverbs are treated with a great realism of detail and distinguished by a robust homespun quality.

51. *HEAD OF ABRAHAM GRAPHEUS, PERHAPS FOR A PENITENT SAINT PETER.* Oil on panel. 26½ x 20½ inches (67.31 x 52.07 cm). COLLECTIONS: Warneck; Baron Leon Pitteurs Hugaerts d'Orange; Mersch; Alberto J. Pani; (given to Detroit by Armand Hammer and Frederic A. Gimbel of New York). EXHIBITION: Fiévez Gallery, Brussels, 1927, No. 69, pl. 12. LITERATURE: M. Rooses, *Jacob Jordaens,* New York, 1908, ill. p. 37; J. S. Held, *"Malerier og Tegninger af Jacob Jordaens i Kunstmuseet," Kunstmuseets Aarsskrift,* Copenhagen, 1939, p. 11; A. J. Pani, *La Segunda Coleccion Pani de Pinturas, Catalogo Descriptivo y Comentado,* Mexico, 1940, No. 21; W. R. Valentiner, "The Penitent Saint Peter," *Bulletin of the Detroit Institute of Arts,* XXIV, No. 2, 1944, pp. 16–18; Detroit Institute of Arts, *Catalogue of Paintings,* Detroit, 1944, p. 71; L. van Puyvelde, *Jordaens,* Paris, 1953, pp. 84, 232; R.-A. d'Hulst, *De Tekeningen van Jacob Jordaens,* Brussels, 1956, p. 86, n. 1.

It was a common practice with Jordaens to paint oil studies of heads from life that became part of his stock for use in his major compositions. They were apparently of especial value to Jordaens, for twenty-four head studies such as the one exhibited here are known to us (van Puyvelde, p. 232). From comparison with a portrait of 1620 by Cornelis de Vos in the Museum in Antwerp (*Catalogue du Musée Royal,* 1948, No. 104) the model for this sketch can be identified as Abraham Grapheus the Elder, Treasurer of the Guild of St. Luke in Antwerp. Jordaens had become a member of the Guild in 1615 and obviously found this man an excellent and accessible model, since he made at least eight separate head studies of Grapheus (van Puyvelde, p. 84; d'Hulst, p. 86, n. 1). Our particular sketch does not appear in any known finished work by Jordaens, but he used a head of Grapheus in the famous picture in Copenhagen of *St. Peter Finding a Stater in the Fish's Mouth,* better known as *The Ferry at Antwerp,* and in *The Offering to Pomona* in the Prado. The association with the Copenhagen picture and the dramatic expression of the head exhibited here have suggested that Jordaens posed Grapheus in the guise of a penitent St. Peter.

Van Dyck also sketched the head of Grapheus and used his studies in larger compositions, for example in *The Descent of the Holy Ghost,* now in Berlin, painted for the Abbaye-aux-Dunes in Bruges (Glück, *Van Dyck,* Stuttgart, 1931, p. 56). One of van Dyck's sketches of Grapheus, now in Berlin (Glück, p. 32), shows the closeness of the relationship betwen van Dyck and Jordaens, for this sketch and one by Jordaens in the Louvre seem to have been painted at the very same sitting, van Dyck painting the model from the right side while Jordaens worked on the left (Valentiner, p. 18). Jordaens evidently owned van Dyck's study, which was later pasted onto a panel and enlarged by Jordaens, who painted in the hands (Valentiner, p. 18). This sketching session with Grapheus is also a valuable aid in dating our Jordaens sketch. We know that van Dyck used some of his studies of Grapheus for the three completed pictures painted in 1619–1620 for the Abbaye-aux-Dunes, and Jordaens must have painted his sketches of Grapheus at about the same time, 1619–1620, a date supported by the appearance of Grapheus in the above-mentioned Cornelis de Vos portrait of 1620. It was only during the period of their early development (*circa* 1616–1620) that van Dyck's and Jordaens' styles were similar, so similar in fact that the attributions of some of the head studies to either artist were once extremely confused (H. Gerson and E. H. Ter Kuile, *Art and Architecture in Belgium,* 1960, p. 127, n. 2). D.W.P.

Lent by The Detroit Institute of Arts

52. *TELEMACHUS LEADS THEOCLYMENUS TO HIS MOTHER PENELOPE.* Gouache, bistre, and water color on paper. Inscribed on lower left: *Jordans.* 11$\frac{3}{16}$ x 20$\frac{1}{16}$ inches (28.3 x 50.7 cm). COLLECTIONS: Crozat, Paris (sale of 1741, No. 856?); Tessin, Stockholm (acquired by the Nationalmuseum in 1761). EXHI-

BITIONS: *Exposition d'un choix de dessins du quinzième au dixhuitième siècle* . . . , Nationalmuseum, Stockholm, 1933, No. 38; *Dutch and Flemish Drawings in the Nationalmuseum and other Swedish Collections,* Nationalmuseum, Stockholm, 1953, No. 129; *Tekeningen van Jakob Jordaens, 1593–1678,* Rubenshuis, Antwerp, 1966, and Museum Boymans-van Beuningen, Rotterdam, 1966–67. LITERATURE: For the latest accounts, with references, see R.-A. d'Hulst, "Jordaens and His Early Activities in the Field of Tapestry," *Art Quarterly,* XIX, 1956, pp. 239–243; and R.-A. d'Hulst, *De Tekeningen van Jakob Jordaens* (Koninklijke Vlaamse Academie voor Wetenschappen, Letteren en Schone Kunsten van België, Klasse der Schone Kunsten, No. 10), Brussels, 1956, No. 39.

This sketch, which reminds us that Jordaens began his career as a tempera painter, is included in the exhibition to show a certain similarity in handling water-color and oil sketching while at the same time revealing the obvious contrasts. The brush moves with an equal speed and flow as in Jordaens' oil sketch shown here (No. 51), but the effect of the gouache naturally depends on the transparency of the medium and the importance of the paper for the over-all tonal values. Instructive for both similarities and differences is a comparison with the brush sketches of Castiglione (Nos. 28, 29), whose oil technique is close to that of water-color.

Our sketch is one of five preserved preparatory studies for an early tapestry cycle by Jordaens of the *History of Ulysses,* deriving from the *Odyssey.* Quickly and effortlessly Jordaens has set down the basic composition and grouping, a symmetrical arrangement in which the Telemachus party bursts into the room from the right, surprising Penelope, placed at the center, and her serving-women at the left; the scene takes place in a light-filled room, with Penelope seated in a corner and the perspective focusing on her. From this sketch Jordaens made a large-scale modello, painted in oil on canvas (117 x 225 cm; Musée Granet, Aix-en-Province, No. 363), that clarifies the composition; from the modello he prepared the cartoon, and this was turned over to the weavers.

The development, from sketch to oil modello to cartoon, is typical of Jordaens' approach to his tapestry designs. Such careful preparation helps us understand that the tapestries were more than mere wall decorations: the Ulysses cycle was not only an illustration of the myth but probably also had a didactic purpose, namely the encouragement of noble and moral feelings (J. S. Held, *Oud Holland,* LXXX, 1965, p.

116). This moral weight is not yet obvious in the sketch where instead we sense the freshness and spontaneity of the first idea.

The inspiration for Jordaens' *History of Ulysses* came from ·the paintings by Primaticcio in the *Galerie d'Ulysse* in Fontainebleau, though Jordaens knew these only at second-hand, either from water-color and gouache drawings made by Rubens *circa* 1630 or from a series of engravings by Theodore van Thulden, published in 1633. Jordaens' activity in tapestry design began *circa* 1635, the approximate date of the Ulysses cycle, and continued until late in the 1650's. The Ulysses cycle proved highly successful and was woven at least twice. No tapestry survives of the first set with the Telemachus and Penelope scene of our sketch, but parts of the composition turn up in tapestries of the second set: in one, Penelope and the Telemachus group were used (Quirinal Palace, Rome), in the other Penelope and her serving-women (Royal Palace, Turin).   D.W.P.

Lent by the Nationalmuseum, Stockholm

ANTHONY VAN DYCK (1599–1641)

The son of a wealthy Antwerp merchant, by 1610 van Dyck was a pupil of Hendrik van Balen, and in 1618 he became a full member of the Antwerp Guild of St. Luke. From 1617–1620 he worked as an assistant in Rubens' studio. After a short trip to England van Dyck went to Italy, where he stayed for about six years, mainly in Genoa. In 1627 he was back in Antwerp, and he was appointed court painter at Brussels in 1630. He returned to England in 1632, and his extraordinarily successful career reached its climax when he was appointed by Charles I "principalle Paynter in ordinary to their Majesties" and knighted by the King. Except for frequent trips to the continent, he remained in London until his death.

53. *BETRAYAL OF CHRIST.* Oil on canvas. 55 x 44½ inches (139.7 x 113 cm). COLLECTIONS: Lord Egremont; Sir Herbert Cook, Doughty House, Richmond, Surrey. (Not the same picture formerly in Erard Coll., sold in Paris in 1832 [Stechow, p. 14, n. 1].) EXHIBITIONS: *Exposition Van Dyck,* Antwerp, 1899, No. 10; Royal Academy, London, 1900, No. 85; *Masterpieces from the Cook Collection of Richmond, England,* Toledo Museum, Toledo, Ohio, 1944–1945, No. 250; *Flemish Art,* Royal Academy, London, 1953–1954, No. 218. LITERATURE: J. Smith, *Catalogue raisonné,* London, 1831, III, No. 18; L. Cust, *Anthony Van Dyck,* London, 1905, pp. 30–31; G. Glück, *Van Dyck: des Meisters Gemälde* (Klassiker der Kunst,

XIII), Stuttgart, 1931, p. 71; M. Delacre, "Le dessin dans l'oeuvre de Van Dyck," *Académie royale de Belgique, Classe des Beaux-Arts, Mémoires,* 2nd series, III, Part I, Brussels, 1934, pp. 67 ff; H. Vey, *Van-Dyck-Studien,* Cologne Dissertation, 1955, pp. 178–209; H. Vey, *Die Zeichnungen Anton Van Dycks,* Brussels, 1962, Nos. 80–86; W. Stechow, "Anthony Van Dyck's 'Betrayal of Christ,' " *Minneapolis Institute of Arts Bulletin,* XLIX, 1960, pp. 4–17; J. S. Held, review of Vey, *Die Zeichnungen Anton Van Dycks,* in *Art Bulletin,* XLVI, 1964, pp. 565–568.

This sketch is one of the most important of van Dyck's early works: it shows his style of *circa* 1620 when he was still in Rubens' studio and had not yet been in Italy. As Stechow pointed out, van Dyck followed St. John's text (18: 1–12), for only St. John names Malchus and Peter as actors in the incident we see in the foreground and identifies the band coming for Christ as carrying "lanterns, torches, and weapons."

The sketch corresponds in almost every detail to a large painting now in the Prado, Madrid (*KdK,* p. 69), and is surely the modello for it. The Madrid picture was in Rubens' collection at the time of his death and was bought in 1641 by Philip IV of Spain. Although the sketch shown here is large, the Madrid picture is twice as wide and two and one-half times as high. Another version, in Lord Methuen's collection in Corsham (*KdK,* p. 70), with Christ and Judas centralized and the Malchus-Peter group eliminated, was probably painted after the Madrid picture. And in a *St. Jerome* (*KdK,* p. 68; present location uncertain) probably made about the same time van Dyck used one of the figures from the composition again: the old man who peers anxiously around Judas to see what is going on.

As the very size of the sketch indicates, van Dyck prepared this composition carefully, and a surprising number of preparatory drawings have survived. He based the composition very closely on a *Betrayal* by Martin de Vos of Antwerp (de Grez Collection, No. 3934, Brussels Museum; engraved by Jan Sadeler, 1582), and at least six of van Dyck's drawings are compositional studies in the development of the design. One of these, now in Hamburg (Kunsthalle; Vey, 1962, fig. 115), is squared for transfer; with all the elements completely worked out, this is surely the final, meticulous study for the oil sketch. Yet this sketch is painted as vigorously and freshly as if the ideas had flowed spontaneously from van Dyck's brush; the canvas shows through in many places and the brush-strokes are broad and free. Clearly van Dyck envied Rubens' ability to sketch out his first ideas in a design that often turned out to be the final one as well, and both his subjects at this time and his preparatory work reveal, as Held has noted (*Art Bulletin,* XLVI, 1964, p. 568), that van Dyck evidently "made an intense effort to prove himself another Rubens." In this sketch we clearly see the results of van Dyck's own desire to imitate the *furia del pennello* of Rubens, but the careful preparation, sheen of glittering light, and nervous excitement belong to van Dyck alone.   s.b.s.

Lent by The Minneapolis Institute of Arts

54. *MAN WEARING A FALLING RUFF.* Oil on canvas. 20¼ x 18 inches (52 x 46 cm). COLLECTION: Presented to the Ashmolean Museum by Mr. Chambers Hall in 1855. EXHIBITIONS: *Works of Art,* Leeds, 1868; *Flemish Art,* Royal Academy, London, 1953–1954, Nos. 443, 444. LITERATURE: P. Buschmann, "Rubens en Van Dyck in het Ashmolean Museum te Oxford," *Onze Kunst,* XXIX, 1916, pp. 48–51; G. Glück, "Van Dyck's Burnt Painting of the Brussels City Council," *Old Master Drawings,* XIV, 1939, pp. 1–4; *Catalogue of Paintings in the Ashmolean Museum,* Oxford, 1961, No. 138. (For the Paris modello see: J. Guiffrey, *Antoine van Dyck,* Paris, 1882, pp. 87–88; R.-A. d'Hulst and H. Vey in Antwerp-Rotterdam Exhibition, *Antoon Van Dyck,* 1960, No. 133; H. Vey, *Die Zeichnungen Anton Van Dycks,* Brussels, 1962, under No. 197; *Le Siècle de Rubens,* Musées Royaux des Beaux-Arts de Belgique, Brussels, 1965, No. 76, with bibliography.)

Van Dyck's *Man Wearing a Falling Ruff* was apparently made in connection with a grisaille oil sketch on panel (Paris, Ecole des Beaux-Arts), showing seven men grouped at either side of a figure of Justice (Pl. 54A). Indeed our sketch appears to be a study for the figure seated immediately to the right of Justice: the heads are turned the same way and the man in the panel is, in fact, the only one of the seven wearing that particular kind of ruff. The Paris oil sketch has been called the modello for Van Dyck's now destroyed group portrait, the *Magistrates of Brussels,* originally located in the Town Hall of Brussels and burnt with the building in 1695. Guiffrey's proposal (pp. 87–88) that the picture was executed between 1634–1635 has been generally accepted; in 1634 van Dyck actually resided in Brussels, living in the house *In't Paradijs* behind the Town Hall. More recently, however, Puyvelde (in *Le siècle de Rubens,* p. 75) has suggested that the commission may have been received during van Dyck's stay in The Netherlands between 1628–1632. Vey, without stating his source (1962, p. 63), noted that the Brussels magistrates paid van Dyck 2.400 florins for the large group portrait on April 15, 1628, but Vey continued to date the destroyed painting between 1634–1635 (p. 268).

Of the three 17th-century sources that describe the picture, two say it had 23 figures and the other more vaguely says 24 or 25 (Vey, 1962, pp. 268–269); if in fact the grisaille sketch in Paris is the modello, clearly it does not give the final form because only seven figures are shown. The painting itself was always described as being a single piece, and thus the 16 missing figures cannot have been represented on adjoining canvases. Van Dyck's sketch in Paris may represent only the six most significant figures in the composition, with the others, like the seventh who leans against a column at the right, to be included later only as half-length figures or portrait-heads in the background. This would make a very crowded composition, however, and it is far more likely that the format of the final picture was much more elongated than the Paris sketch. And so the Paris sketch should most probably be regarded as an early stage in the development rather than the modello proper.

Our sketch shows the brilliance and economy of van Dyck's brush. With only a few strokes he suggests the expansive form of the figure and his strength of personality. Obviously he must have made other sketches for the final paintings, and some of these have been identified —for example a companion head at the Ashmolean—or at least proposed as belonging to this picture. Interestingly enough, these sketches include portraits both in oil and in drawing. (The art-historical problems are of course great. For a discussion of the other heads, see Buschmann, *Onze Kunst,* figs. opp. p. 50, who was the first to connect the Ashmolean heads with the Paris sketch; d'Hulst and Vey, *Exhib. Cat.,* 1960, p. 167; Glück, p. 4; and Vey, 1962, pls. 241–242 for the same drawings discussed by Glück.)   s.b.s.

Lent by the Visitors of the Ashmolean Museum, Oxford

REMBRANDT VAN RIJN (1606–1669)

Born, raised, and first trained in Leiden, Rembrandt spent a short but significant period with Pieter Lastman in Amsterdam. His independent career began in Leiden (1624–1625); in 1631 he moved to Amsterdam where he stayed until his death. A painter, draughtsman, and etcher, he handled every kind of subject but established his reputation as a portraitist in the 1630's, reaching a climax in *The Night Watch* of 1642. In the 1640's, following the death of his wife Saskia, Rembrandt turned away from the world, and the exuberance of his early style yielded to calmer, more classicising structure, more concerned with inner states of being. His work grew progressively more profound in spiritual depth and power right to the end.

55. *HEAD OF AN OLD MAN WITH A BEARD*. Oil on panel. Inscribed on back: *Gemeente Museum 1906*. 9½ x 7½ inches (24 x 19 cm). COLLECTIONS: A. Vollon, Paris; F. Kleinberger, Paris; Marcus Kappel, Berlin. EXHIBITIONS: Leiden, 1906, No. 53a; Berlin, 1909, No. 109. LITERATURE: W. R. Valentiner, *Rembrandt: des Meisters Gemälde* (Klassiker der Kunst, II), Stuttgart, 1909, p. 504; C. Hofstede de Groot, *Beschreibendes und kritisches Verzeichnis der Werke der hervorragendsten holländischen Maler des XVII. Jahrhunderts,* Esslingen-Paris, 1907–1928, VI, No. 366; W. R. Valentiner, *Rembrandt Paintings in America,* New York, 1931, pl. 162; A. Bredius, *Rembrandt Gemälde,* Vienna, 1935, pl. 261; K. Bauch, *Rembrandt Gemälde,* Berlin, 1966, pl. 245.

Rembrandt is unusual among his contemporary Dutch artists for making oil sketches at all, and even in his work they are not common. He sketched a few subject pieces in oil and studies of heads. Of these, old men were favorite subjects, and our sketch is typical in being painted in oil on panel in a small size. In general the sketches were true preparations; for the *St. Matthew* of 1661 (Louvre; Bauch, No. 231), for example, four oil sketches have come down to us (Bredius, pls. 302–305).

The sketch here exhibited has not yet been identified with a specific picture. Recently Bauch, on the basis of a photograph only, suggested a stylistic comparison with the kneeling old man in the *Circumcision* of 1661 to establish the date (National Gallery of Art, Washington; Bauch, No. 93). Valentiner dated the sketch slightly later, while Hofstede de Groot and Bredius put it to *circa* 1650–1655. In any case, there is no doubt that the sketch belongs to Rembrandt's full maturity. With a few strokes of the brush he models the form and splashes on a light that glows upon the surface; the impasto creates the textures and concentrates the lights on the head and shoulder. The lights and the surprisingly rich colors draw our attention away from the face, that of an old and weary man who bows his head in reverie as he turns away from the light. The sympathy with old people whose natural ambience is a soft and comforting shadow is characteristic of Rembrandt in the 1650's and 1660's, while the technique is a development from his earliest years, deriving ultimately from the Dutch followers of Cara-vaggio.   D.W.P.

Lent by Mr. and Mrs. John Hay Whitney, New York

France

CHARLES LE BRUN (1619–1690)

Charles Le Brun, son of the sculptor Nicholas, began his career at thirteen as an apprentice to François Perrier, later studied with Simon Vouet, and in 1642 went to Rome where he absorbed the styles of Sacchi and above all of Poussin. Upon his return to Paris in 1646, he immediately became a leading force in French art, help-ing to found the Académie in 1648 and establishing his reputation with decorative schemes for noble patrons. In 1660 Louis XIV called Le Brun to Fontainebleau, where he won the king's favor with his painting of *The Family of Darius before Alexander*. He entered the service of the king, under the protection of Colbert, and in 1662 was named *premier peintre du roi*. The king entrusted Le Brun with the decoration of Versailles, the symbol of his reign, and Le Brun's position consequently became, until the death of Colbert in 1683, that of virtual dictator over the arts in France.

56. *ALLEGORY OF THE CAPTURE OF GHENT BY LOUIS XIV IN 1678.*
Oil on canvas, 25¼ x 41¾ inches (64 x 106 cm). COLLECTIONS: Arnaud; acquired
by Troyes in 1847. EXHIBITIONS: *L'art de Versailles,* Musée de l'Orangerie, Paris,
1932, No. 39; *The Age of Louis XIV,* Royal Academy, London, 1958, No. 171; *Le
XVIIᵉ siècle français,* Petit Palais, Paris, 1958, No. 79; *The Splendid Century,*
National Gallery of Art, Washington, Toledo Museum of Art, Metropolitan Museum
of Art, New York, 1960–61, No.97; *Charles Le Brun, 1619–1690,* Château de Versailles, 1963, No. 38. LITERATURE: H. Jouin, *Charles Le Brun et les arts sous
Louis XIV,* Paris, 1889, pp. 283, 505; F. Engerand, ed., *Inventaire des tableaux du
roy rédigé en 1709 et 1710 par Nicolas Bailly,* Paris, 1899, No. 3; P. Marcel, *Charles
Le Brun,* Paris, 1909, pp. 94, 167; Musée de Troyes, *Catalogue des tableaux,* 1911,
No. 163; *Metropolitan Museum of Art Bulletin,* XIX, 1961, p. 235, fig. 8; C. Mau-
mené and L. d'Harcourt, *Iconographie des rois de France* (Archives de l'art français,
XVI), 1932, II, p. 267, No. 405. See also J. Roussel, *Monographie des palais &
parcs de Versailles et des Trianons,* Paris (n.d.), pl. 124; *La Grande Galérie de
Versailles, et les deux salons peints par Charles Le Brun,* Paris, 1752, pls. 1, 6 (engraved by J. B. Massé). (For a drawing by Le Brun showing the whole composition
with its architectural framework, see P. de Nolhac, *Histoire du château de Versailles,* Paris, 1911, II, pl. opp. p. 144.)

This sketch is typical of Le Brun's careful preparation of work for his
greatest patron and his greatest monument, since it was done for the
last large compartment of the ceiling of the Galérie des Glaces on the
side of the Salon de la Paix at Versailles. The picture depicts, allegor-
ically, the capture of Ghent by the French in 1678. Louis XIV had
gone to Flanders and received the keys of the city of Ghent, which had
surrendered to Maréchal d'Humières. The king, as Jupiter supported
by an eagle, holds a bolt of lightning in one hand and a shield em-
blazoned with the head of Gorgon in the other. Louis is accompanied
by Military Vigilance (an arrow in her hand), Secrecy (carrying her
helmet), Glory and Fame. At the left, Terror, with a dagger in her
hand, blows her trumpet. To the right, Minerva pulls the keys away
from the City of Ghent. She is accompanied by the Province of Flanders, recognizable by her native dress and black mantle (indicating that
this event took place under the government of the widow of Philip IV).
Below are the captive cities of Ypres, Cambrai and Valenciennes, designated by their escutcheons. In the upper right, the Maréchal, per-
sonified as Mars, combats Discord. The subject and the allegorical form
of its narration follow Louis XIV's own desires. Originally the Grande
Galérie was to be devoted to Apollo, emblematic of the *Roi-Soleil,* and
the second suggestion was a cycle of the Labors of Hercules, whose

achievements were to symbolize those of Louis XIV. It is typical of the king's pride and sense of glory that he should abandon mythological disguisse in favor of allegories depicting his own person and deeds.

Stylistically the sketch expresses Le Brun's artistic convictions: a professed classicism and clarity of the parts, tempered by a more dramatic lighting and warmth that he disallowed in his theory. Le Brun put his large studio to work on the pictures of the gallery at the end of 1679, the first piece was temporarily uncovered in July of 1681, and the huge ensemble was completed by the end of 1684.

The sketch is first noted in an inventory taken at Le Brun's house shortly after his death in 1690, where it is called a sketched and unfinished picture. Along with all the other works found in Le Brun's home, this piece passed into the collections of the crown where it was noted in 1709–10. Between the years of these two inventories the sketch was cut down some two inches in height and width. As did the other sketches for the Grande Galérie, this piece passed into private hands until, in 1847, it was bought by the Société Académique de l'Aube for its present owners. Sketches for other compartments are now in the Musée de Versailles, the Musée Vivenel at Compiègne and the Musée des Beaux-Arts in Auxerre.   M.C.A.

Lent by the Musée des Beaux-Arts et Société Académique de l'Aube, Troyes

CHARLES DE LA FOSSE (1636–1716)

Charles de la Fosse was born in Paris and was a student first of the engraver François Chauveau and then of Le Brun. On a royal pension obtained by influence, he worked in Rome from 1658 to 1660 and in Venice from 1660 to 1663 when he returned to Paris and soon won fresco commissions. La Fosse entered the Académie in 1673 and was made a professor the following year. In 1690 Lord Montague called him to London to decorate his house. Charles II was so impressed with the result that he asked La Fosse to work at Hampton Court, but he declined and returned to Paris to paint the cupola and pendentives of the church of Les Invalides. In 1699 he was elected director of the Académie. Eleven years later he decorated the apse of the chapel at Versailles.

57. *THE RISING OF THE SUN, FOR THE SALON OF APOLLO AT VER-SAILLES.* Oil on canvas. 39 inches in diameter (101 cm). COLLECTIONS: Prince de Conti sale, 8 April 1777, No. 596; Mercier; Lemonnier (bought by the city of Rouen in 1822). EXHIBITIONS: *Chefs-d'oeuvre des musées de province, Musée de l'Orangerie,* Paris, 1931, No. 26; *Centenaire de Versailles,* 1937; *The Age of Louis XIV,* Royal Academy, London, 1958, No. 221; *Le XVIIᵉ siècle français,* Petit Palais, Paris, 1958, No. 56; *The Splendid Century,* National Gallery of Art, Washington, Toledo Museum of Art, and Metropolitan Museum of Art, New York, 1960–61, No. 125. LITERATURE: E. Minet, *Musée de Rouen, Catalogue des ouvrages. . . ,* Rouen, 1911, No. 518; latest study by M. Stuffman, "Charles de La Fosse," *Gazette des Beaux-Arts,* LXIV, 1964, pp. 70–76, No. 18; full references in P. Rosenberg, *Tableaux français du XVIIᵉᵐᵉ siècle et italiens des XVIIᵉᵐᵉ et XVIIIᵉᵐᵉ siècles,* Paris, 1966, No. 51.

La Fosse worked in the *Grands Appartements* of Versailles between 1671 and 1680 (J. Guiffrey, ed., *Comptes des bâtiments. . . ,* Paris, 1881, I, *passim*), and this is a sketch for the ceiling of one of the principal rooms, the *Salon d'Apollon.* Dedicated to the sun, the room celebrates Louis XIV as Sun King and the picture honors Louis-Apollo, bringing light to the world as he rides over the vault of heaven. The zodiac, acting as a kind of balustrade, is associated with the seasons: Spring with putti and flowers, Summer with a sickle, Autumn with a Bacchic group and a basket of grapes, and Winter with sleeping figures. The Morning Star above heralds the rising sun, while Minerva, banishing Falsehood and Discord, clears Apollo's path.

Although this allegory seems rich enough to modern tastes and the artist had already thought out the problems in another, probably earlier sketch (Musée Cantini, Marseille, No. 647), La Fosse—or the king—was still not satisfied. In the final picture the zodiac is eliminated, the Seasons are shifted, Apollo is made still more prominent and is now endowed with the figures of France and Magnanimity, thus spelling out the identification of Louis with Apollo. The specific emphasis on Louis may point to a date close to a particularly triumphant year, 1678, and to the moment when Apollo was rejected as a subject for the *Grande Galérie,* for which the architectural designs were accepted only in September of 1678.

The iconographic changes also meant compositional changes. The sketch here derives ultimately from Guercino's famous *Aurora* as reworked by Vouet in his *Rising of the Moon,* but the actual ceiling painting relies on Reni's *Aurora.* In either case the evidence of La

Fosse's Italian years remains evident and the light, bright colors, gently introducing the Rococo palette, reflect his study of Correggio and Veronese. The final composition is undoubtedly clearer and more planimetric, a stylistic change that hints at the intrusion of Le Brun, the master decorator of Versailles.   M.C.A.

Lent by the Musée des Beaux-Arts, Rouen

HYACINTHE RIGAUD (1659–1743)

Born in Perpignan, Rigaud did not settle in Paris until 1681. Following the advice of Le Brun, he changed from history painting to portraiture and became the leading portrait painter during the successive reigns of Louis XIV, the Regent Philip of Orléans, and Louis XV. Polished in his depiction of the rich court panoply, Rigaud achieved a fresh and more penetrating characterization in his unofficial portraits.

58. *PORTRAIT OF THE DUC D'ESTRÉES.* Oil on canvas. 20½ x 16⅛ inches (51.5 x 40.8 cm). COLLECTION: de Valcourt. EXHIBITIONS: *French Paintings of the Time of Louis XIII and Louis XIV,* Wildenstein & Co., 1946, No. 46; *French Painting, 1100–1900,* Carnegie Institute, Pittsburgh, 1951, No. 71; *French Paintings,* Vassar College, 1952; *Masterworks from University and College Art Collections,* The University of Kansas Museum of Art, 1958, No. 48; *The Age of Elegance: The Rococo and Its Effect,* Baltimore Museum of Art, 1959, No. 29; *Smith College Loan Exhibition,* The Arts Club of Chicago, 1961, No. 20; *Portraits from the Collection of the Smith College Museum of Art,* Northampton, 1962, No. 5. LITERATURE: J. Roman, *Le Livre de raison du peintre Hyacinthe Rigaud,* Paris, 1919, p. 22; F. Hartt, "Two French Baroque Paintings," *Smith College Museum of Art Bulletin,* Nos. 25–28, June, 1947, pp. 18–21. For the duke, see A. Richer, *Vies de Jean d'Estrées . . . et de Victor-Marie d'Estrées. . . ,* Paris, 1789, *passim;* E. Bonaffé, *Dictionnaire des amateurs français au 17ᵉ siècle,* Paris, 1884; Georges Duplessis, *Les Audran,* Paris, n.d., p. 54.

Besides creating a lasting image of the Bourbon court, Rigaud has left us a record of the activities in his studio. Although his account book, the *Livre de Raison,* is not complete or consistent, it provides an insight into his working methods. In it Rigaud frequently distinguishes finished portraits from the preparatory stages, sketch (*ébauche*) and drawing (*dessein*). Furthermore, originals are differentiated from copies, for which he often mentions specific studio hands. The haunting portrait of the Duc d'Estrées here on view is a fine example of one of Rigaud's spontaneous sketches. Dr. George Van Derveer Gallenkamp, who has kindly supplied information from the monograph on Rigaud he is preparing, dates this unfinished portrait *circa* 1690, citing an entry in the *Livre de Raison* for the year 1690: "Mons le compte Destréz— 115 livres." Dr. Gallenkamp also considers the wig style appropriate to persons of official status between *circa* 1685 and 1700 and suggests a stylistic resemblance between this study from nature of the duke and a portrait in the Musée Carnavalet, Paris.

Another fine oil study of a head left unfinished is that of the Marquis Jean-Octave de Villars in the Toledo Museum of Art. Both the Toledo and Smith oil sketches display a fluency of brushwork that is startling compared with the finesse of Rigaud's completed paintings. This treatment would seem to relate Rigaud's oil sketches to the work of his contemporary and rival, Nicolas Largillière.

Well known for his brilliant exploits as naval commander, Victor-Marie, Duc d'Estrées (1660–1737), succeeded his father as "maréchal de France, vice-amiral, et vice-roi de l'Amérique." He was also, according to Bonnaffé, something of an art collector and an ardent bibliophile, and his intellectual pursuits were crowned by his election to the membership of the Académie Francaise. Bonnaffé also mentions that Largillière painted Victor-Marie's portrait, known only in an engraving by Jean Audran with the inscription, "N. Largillière pinx., J. Audran scul." The sitter is not identified, but it is almost certainly the same Victor-Marie, Duc d'Estrées, about 20 years older than in the sketch of this exhibition. He has the same large, hypnotic eyes, heavy lids, long, aristocratic nose, but a more pronounced double chin and a powdered wig. Reference may also be made to the engraving of the duke used as frontispiece to his biography by A. Richer. Though rather crudely executed, the features still bear some resemblance to the splendid oil sketch by Rigaud.   C.L.

Lent by the Smith College Museum of Art, Northampton, Massachusetts

ALEXANDRE-FRANÇOIS DESPORTES (1661–1743)

Born in Champigneulles (Champagne), Desportes was sent to Paris at the age of twelve and entrusted to the care and training of his innkeeper uncle. There his talent for painting emerged, and he was apprenticed to the Flemish *animalier* Nicasius Bernaert, with whom he remained until Bernaert's death in 1678. Although still very young, Desportes now set out on his own. For two years (1695–96) he served as portraitist to the court of Poland; but when he returned to Paris he resumed painting animals. Even his reception piece for the Académie in 1699 reflected his devotion—a *Self Portrait as a Sportsman*. From 1700 on, he was employed by the crown at Versailles, Marly and Meudon, at the Gobelins and at various châteaux; he remained popular up to his death in Paris in 1743.

59. *CLOUD STUDY*. Oil on paper mounted on cardboard. 11 1/16 x 13 inches (28 x 33 cm). EXHIBITIONS: *Paysages de François Desportes (1661–1743): Études peintes d'après nature,* Musée National de Compiègne, 1961, No. 2; *Grands ébénistes et menuisiers parisiens du XVIIIe siècle,* Musée des Arts Décoratifs, Paris, 1955–56 (but Desportes' name is not mentioned in the catalogue).

In 1784 Louis XVI purchased some animal and flower studies by Desportes from the artist's nephew. These were to serve as models for the decoration of porcelain at the Sèvres works. Included in the purchase, apparently by accident, were several landscapes of which our exhibit was one. Desportes used some of them as backgrounds in animal paintings, first in 1700 but also later, and the sketches have consequently been dated 1690–1700.

Were this date incorrect and the sketch assigned to Desportes' last years, it would still remain the earliest known cloud study painted in oil in the history of art. Alexander Cozens (1717–86) and Willem van de Velde (1633–1707) did such studies in chalk or wash, and there exist three rare drawings of cloud studies, sometimes attributed to Claude (Curtis O. Baer Collection; Teyler Museum, Haarlem; Kupferstichkabinett, Berlin). But none have the startling modernity of vision and immediacy of impact that Desportes' economic handling of the liquid brush impart to this sketch. In Paris only Valenciennes (1750–1819) followed Desportes in subject and technique, and six cloud studies by Valenciennes in the Louvre, dating between 1778 and 1786, show the same little stretch of ground at the bottom, an orienting horizon line that gives a sense of scale to the open sky.

Like the later Impressionists, Desportes worked outdoors when making his landscape sketches (Pl. 59A), for his son reported that his father carried his brushes, palette, and portable easel right into the fields, never making a country visit without this equipment. Painters had been urged to study the effects of sky and clouds by the theoretician Roger de Piles, but Desportes' is no technical learning process. His sketch reveals a profound love of nature, hardly matched by any artist in Western Europe before Constable. M.C.A.

Lent by the Manufacture Nationale de Sèvres

FRANÇOIS BOUCHER (1703–1770)

A native Parisian, Boucher studied first with François le Moyne. He won the *Prix de Rome,* and spent the years 1727 to 1731 in Italy. Upon his return to France, he rose through the influence of Mme. de Pompadour to become Director of the Gobelins tapestry works in 1755. Ten years later he was the Director of the French Academy, as well as First Painter to the King. With his gay and delicate style, Boucher brought the Olympian gods into the aura of the boudoir. An indefatigable artist, he also worked as an illustrator, engraver and decorator, designing tapestries, furniture and chinoiserie. Boucher was the most brilliant Rococo artist of the Age of Louis XV.

60. *LA PÊCHE CHINOISE.* Oil on canvas. 15⅞ x 18¾ inches (40.5 x 47 cm).

61. *LA CHASSE CHINOISE.* Oil on canvas. 15¾ x 18¾ inches (40 x 47 cm). COLLECTIONS: Bergeret de Grandcourt (sale, March 24, 1786, Nos. 55, 56); the whole series was acquired by Pierre-Adrien Pâris, who bequeathed it to the library of Besançon; the set entered the museum in 1843. EXHIBITIONS: *Le paysage français de Poussin à Corot,* Palais des Beaux-Arts, Paris, 1925, Nos. 25, 26; *Schönheit des XVIII. Jahrhunderts,* Kunsthaus, Zurich, 1955 (*La Pêche*—No. 31; *La Chasse*—No. 32); *European Masters of the Eighteenth Century,* Royal Academy, London, 1954–1955 (*La Chasse*—No. 450); *Besançon, le plus ancien musée de France,* Musée des Arts Décoratifs, Paris, 1957, Nos. 12, 13; *Le siècle du Rococo,* Residenz, Munich, 1958 (*La Pêche*—No. 14); *François Boucher,* Galerie Cailleux, Paris, 1964, Nos. 22, 23. LITERATURE: "Inventaire mss. de Pâris," 1806, No. 89 (the set); the set also listed in the various editions of the *Catalogue du Musée des Beaux-Arts* of Besançon: 1844, Nos. 15–23; (*I.R.A.M.*) 1889, pp. 19, 20; Magnin, 1919, p. 98; Chudant,

1929, Nos. 14–22; *Cat. des Salles de Peintures,* 1949, Nos. 134–142. For later references, see Cailleux exhibition (listed above); and H. Honour, *Chinoiserie, The Vision of Cathay,* New York, 1962, p. 93.

La Chasse chinoise and *La Pêche chinoise* are two of eight charming sketches that Boucher designed in 1742 to be woven into tapestries at Beauvais. In the eighteenth century the enthusiasm for genuine Chinese *objets d'art* led to the creation of fantasies which had an oriental flavor but were still fundamentally French and Rococo. In this case Boucher probably adapted the costumes and accessories from the drawings of the Jesuit father Attiret, who had been in China. Instead of portraying the ceremony of the Emperor's court, Boucher chose to depict a more leisurely pastoral setting, giving an exotic disguise to some of the more normal French pastimes. In addition to the hunting and fishing scenes exhibited here there were sketches of a Chinese marriage, an audience with the Emperor, an Emperor's feast, a fair, a garden, a dance, and a "curiosity." The sketches were worked into cartoons by Jean Joseph Dumons, and the designs were engraved by Huquier. The tapestries were a tremendous success. One set decorated the apartment of Mme. de Pompadour. Louis XV sent another set to the Emperor K'ang Hsi, in order to foster good relations between France and China.   C.L.

Lent by the Musée des Beaux-Arts, Besançon

62. *THE ABDUCTION OF PROSERPINA.* Oil on canvas. 22⅝ x 18¾ inches (58 x 48 cm). Signed: *Boucher, 1769.* COLLECTIONS: Probably Vicomte E. de Plinval, 1846; Comte de Silguy (bequeathed to the museum in 1864). LITERATURE: Gauguet and Hombron, *Catalogue des tableaux exposés dans les galeries du musée de la ville de Quimper,* Brest, 1873, No. 536 (as *Neptune and Amphitrite*); A. Michel, *François Boucher,* Paris, 1906, p. 15, No. 220.

Formerly called *Neptune and Amphitrite* or *Neptune and Amymone,* the subject of Boucher's oval grisaille is actually from another tale of Ovid, the Abduction of Proserpina (*Metamorphoses,* V, 346 ff.). Boucher, in an easy but careful way, often inserts attributes in his designs to help identify the gods. In his versions of Europa, Danaë, and Leda and the Swan, he sometimes includes an eagle to specify Jupiter. In the tapestry designs for Neptune and Amymone, Boucher sees to it that the sea god holds a trident. The traditional manner of identifying

Pluto is his regal scepter, a bident, which in the case of this sketch is displayed by a putto. Pluto was attracted by the goddess Proserpina, who had been quietly picking flowers in a Sicilian meadow, and, as is shown here, he abducted her to become Queen of the Underworld. According to Ovid, the water nymph Cyane deplored Pluto's rough manner of wooing his bride, and Cyane is seen in the Quimper grisaille gesturing in mild protest.

Boucher did many drawings for Beauvais and later for the Gobelins tapestries representing the Loves of the Gods. In 1749 he designed an *Abduction of Proserpina* (M. Fenaille, *François Boucher,* 1925, p. 88) that was woven many times. He continually supplied new drawings for tapestries, sometimes in grisaille. In 1763 and 1764 he did four more pictures of the Loves of the Gods—in oval format—for the Gobelins manufactury. These four paintings, *Vertumnus and Pomona, Aurora and Cephalus, Neptune and Amymone, Venus and Vulcan,* also represent the Four Elements (Fenaille, *Etat général des tapisseries . . . des Gobelins, 1600–1900,* 1907, IV, pp. 229 ff). The records are not complete as to how many of these designs produced by Boucher were in fact executed, but the probability is strong that our *Abduction of Proserpina* of 1769 was conceived as another double reference: to the love of the god and, since the putto at the right brandishes a torch leading to Hades, to the element of fire.   c.l.

Lent by the Musée Municipal des Beaux-Arts, Quimper

63. *DANAË.* Oil on canvas. 11⅜ x 13¾ inches (29 x 35 cm). COLLECTION: Not traceable before 1961; Cailleux Collection, Paris. EXHIBITION: *François Boucher,* Galerie Cailleux, Paris, 1964, No. 72. LITERATURE: Anon., "La vie des objets: une esquisse retrouvée de François Boucher," *Connaissance des arts,* No. 147, May, 1964, p. 49.

The *Danaë* is executed with far greater force than the *chinoiseries* that Boucher had done earlier with great delicacy of style. It is difficult to tell the thick, loosely painted technique of Boucher from that of his student of a golden shower, and she consequently became the mother of Perseus Fragonard at this time, *circa* 1755–1760 (cf. Fragonard's *Gimblette,* No. 70). Boucher, who made designs for tapestries of the Loves of the Gods, often chose themes from Ovid. Jupiter visited Danaë in the form

(*Metamorphoses,* IV, 610 ff). A preparatory chalk drawing for the figure of Danaë, now in the Kress Collection, National Gallery, Washington (Pl. 63A), is surprisingly careful in comparison with the brilliant freshness and immediacy of the sketch. Boucher shifted her position only slightly and added the shower of gold and a cupid. An earlier *Danaë* in the Atheneum, Helsinki, follows Ovid's *Ars Amatoria* (III, 415) more closely, including her guardian, an old lady; this painting, *circa* 1740, is much airier, and the figure of Danaë is quite dainty. Closer in style to the Stockholm oil sketch is a Boucher drawing in the Musée Bonnat, Bayonne, where Jupiter's eagle is present and the half-draped young Danaë is turned in the direction of the spectator. A small painting in the Musée Cognacq-Jay, Paris, attributed to the shop of Boucher as a pendant to a painting of *Cupid and Psyche,* displays a half-draped Danaë surrounded by three *amorini.* The shower of gold has already settled.   C.L.

Lent by the Nationalmuseum, Stockholm

JEAN-FRANÇOIS DE TROY (1679–1752)

Son and student of the well-known artist François de Troy, Jean-François was born in 1679. He received only a second prize at the Académie in 1697, but, through his father, he was given a pension to go to Rome where he arrived in 1699. He was soon forced to leave and traveled to Venice, Padua, Verona and Pisa, staying in Pisa for three years before returning to Paris *circa* 1706. A *bon vivant,* he enjoyed painting *fêtes* and fancy pictures but remained eager for high office and happily accepted the directorship of the French Academy in Rome in 1738. He was replaced by Natoire in 1752 and died less than a month later.

64. *THE CAPTURE OF THE GOLDEN FLEECE.* 21¾ x 31¾ inches (56 x 80 cm). COLLECTIONS: de Troy sale, 1764, No. 286; Ribes Christofle (1928 sale, No. 55); Jacques Seligmann; Cailleux. EXHIBITIONS: Galerie Georges-Petit, Paris, 1928; *Exposition des esquisses maquettes, projets et ébauches de l'école française du XVIIIe siècle,* Galerie Cailleux, Paris, 1934, No. 23; *Vasari to Tiepolo,* Hazlitt Gallery, London, 1952, No. 13; *Il settecento a Roma,* Rome, 1959, No. 631; *Seventeenth and Eighteenth Century Oil Sketches,* Hazlitt Gallery, London, 1961, No. 22. LITERATURE: G. Brière, "Detroy," in L. Dimier, *Les peintres français du XVIIIe siècle,* Paris, 1930, II, No. 57. (For the tapestries, see M. Fenaille, *Etat général des tapisseries de la manufacture des Gobelins,* Paris, 1907, IV, pp. 99–135 and pl. opp. p. 122.)

Because he had no patron in the right circles to win him royal commissions in the 1730's, de Troy proposed to design instead a set of tapestries for the Gobelins on the story of Esther. Their success led to the commission of another series, on the story of Jason and Medea, which de Troy received when Oudry failed to turn out any sketches. For source material he turned to Ovid and to Euripides and Seneca, and he handled the subjects easily and gracefully. De Troy began work on his sketches in December of 1742. In our sketch, the first in the series, he presents the myth as a straightforward lively narrative packed with incident. Jason, with one foot on the sleeping dragon, is about to cut away the golden fleece. Medea is a pretty princess who gestures in surprise as she gazes at her hero. Behind them a bustling mob prepares to sail away. The élan and spontaneous brush create a scene of striking charm.

Our sketch along with the others of the series was sent to Paris, but the Gobelins returned them to Rome requesting the correction of compositional shortcomings. De Troy complied: he solidified the structure clarified the gestures, and emphasized Jason rather than Medea. But in the process he turned the movement and sense of an excited moment in the sketches into a staid and placid monumentality that pervades both the cartoons and the tapestries, as a comparison of our sketch with the tapestry demonstrates (Pl. 64A; Victoria and Albert Museum, London). The cartoons were all completed in 1746 but did not arrive in Paris until two years later where they were exhibited in the Salon of 1748. They were woven with borders designed in Paris. Our scene shows a rock and a cartouche, both not present in the sketch, the former inscribed *De Troy a Rome, 1743,* and the latter containing the legend: "Jason made the dragon drowsy, raises the Golden Fleece and leaves with Medea." The tapestries proved a tremendous success and the *Golden Fleece* was produced eleven times.   M.C.A.

Lent by Mr. and Mrs. Eliot Hodgkin, London

JEAN BARBAULT (1718–1766)

The parish register of Viarmes (Seine-et-Oise) certifies that Barbault was born in 1718, correcting the date of *circa* 1705 usually found in the literature. He studied in Paris with Restout, and the Académie des Beaux-Arts sent him to Rome, where he arrived by 1748. Here he may have studied with Subleyras. J.-F. de Troy, then director of the French Academy in Rome, secured him an extension of his pension in 1750, but his disorderly life, debts, and a marriage (against academy rules) forced him to leave in 1753. He remained in Rome until his death, but, obliged to abandon painting for want of cash, he worked for publishers, engraving views of Rome somewhat in the manner of Piranesi with whom he once had collaborated.

65. *ST. JEROME IN THE DESERT*. Oil on canvas. 13⅜ x 8⅞₁₆ inches (34 x 22 cm). EXHIBITIONS: *Il settecento a Roma*, Rome, 1959, No. 650 (as Joseph-Marie Vien); *I francesi a Roma*, Rome, 1961; No. 578. LITERATURE: R. Longhi, "Il Goya romano e la 'Cultura di via Condotti'," *Paragone*, V, 1954, No. 53, pl. 17b (as Pierre or Vien).

This and a similar sketch of *A Priest in Prayer Before an Altar* (Busiri Vivi Collection) were reattributed to Barbault in 1961, by Charles Sterling, after a long process of careful refinement. Best known for his later Roman *vedute*, Barbault had earlier established a reputation as a painter of costume pieces. He did a set of 20 small pictures of figures from a Turkish Masquerade in 1748, a sketch for a projected masquerade in 1751 (Besançon), and, on commission, 12 painted studies of Italian costumes. His extant pictures are rare, but obviously his talent flourished in sketches like the one shown here, small pictures, mainly of single figures, painted in a lively and abstract manner. The *Priest in Prayer* mentioned above and *A Cistercian Nun* (Lord Leconfield Collection), signed and dated 1750, show religious figures that may also be classsified as costume pieces (cf. J. Picault, *Bulletin de la société de l'histoire de l'art français*, 1951, pp. 27–31). Yet on occasion Barbault did paint serious religious subjects, as we know from a *Baptism of Constantine* (Lille), signed and dated 1758. Our sketch clearly belongs in this category; it shows St. Jerome in traditional attitude accompanied by his lion, barely sketched in on the right. Barbault may well have intended to do a series of single saints, combining the traditional subjects with his taste for costume studies.   M.C.A.

Lent by N. U. l'Architetto Andrea Busiri Vici, Rome

JOSEPH-MARIE VIEN (1716–1809)

Vien was one of the most successful painters in France in the second half of the 18th century. A partial list of his honors and positions includes the *Prix de Rome* in 1743; Agréé (1751), Member (1754), and Professor (1759) of the Royal Academy in Paris; Director of the French Academy in Rome (1776–1781); and, again in Paris, Director of the Royal Academy and first painter to the King in 1789. His style, which turned to the antique for inspiration, was praised by government officials as well as by the art critic-philosopher Diderot. His painting marked the turning away from the previously dominant Rococo, and Vien is probably most famous as the teacher and precursor of Jacques Louis David.

66. *AN INVOCATION SCENE.* Oil on paper mounted on canvas. 11⅜ x 8¼ inches (29 x 21 cm). COLLECTION: Lemonnier (bought by the city of Rouen in 1822). LITERATURE: E. Minet, *Musée de Rouen*, Rouen, 1911, No. 794.

This sketch shows a bishop who gestures to the poor as he prays to a martyr saint to invoke the aid of the Madonna and Child. The freedom and movement of the brush-stroke in our sketch is common to the French painters who worked in Italy, such as La Fosse in the 17th century and J.-F. de Troy later, both of whom influenced Vien's work. But Vien's study in Rome of Domenichino, Guercino, and Reni encouraged a broader and more solid style of painting that is typical of his finished pictures. The looseness we see in the work here exhibited, where the free and visible stroke animates both forms and surface, occurs only in a few of Vien's sketches apart from ours, for example in a sketch dated 1763 of *A Girl Watering a Pot of Flowers,* now in the museum at Béziers (Lugand, *Revue du Louvre*, XIV, Nos. 4–5, 1964, p. 269). In both works the handling is similar. The brush flies rapidly over the surface, dots of paint suggest the features, and almost formless strokes abstract the hands. Only in the detail of the architecture on the right is there a hint of the predominantly classicizing taste that marks his official, completed works of exactly the same period.

The kneeling bishop has yet to be identified, but the floating saint— through whom the aid of the Virgin and Child is invoked—is most probably Joseph. The face is of a type usual for him, and many images are known in which Mary presents him with the Christ Child (E. Mâle,

L'Art religieux après le Concile de Trente, 1932, p. 321). A putto with martyr's palms hovers over the saint's head; although he was not martyred, the question of his classification among the martyrs had been argued since the point had been raised in the 16th-century history of St. Joseph by Isolanus (I. Vallejo, *Life of St. Joseph,* 1861, pp. 204 ff). Provocatively enough, the scheme of this sketch from the Rouen museum is analogous to a briefly described picture noted by Mâle as being in Rouen Cathedral (p. 321, n. 3).   C.L. and J.K.

Lent by the Musée des Beaux-Arts, Rouen

JEAN-BAPTISTE GREUZE (1725–1805)

Jean-Baptiste Greuze was born at Tournus. He began his artistic studies early in life, mainly at Lyons, and went to Paris *circa* 1750. In 1755 he left for Italy but returned to Paris in 1757 and never made another major trip. Greuze specialized in sentimental and moralizing pictures that won him a great following, but he never reached the heights of academic acceptance which he sought. In spite of the Revolution and a painfully bad marriage, he was active until his death in 1805.

67. *THE SURPRISED HOUSEKEEPER.* Oil on canvas. 19^{11}⁄$_{16}$ x 10^{3}⁄$_{16}$ inches (50 x 28 cm). COLLECTIONS: Chiff sale, 1867, No. 28; M. Grobet Labadié, bought *chez* Mathey, Paris, 1905. (Because it is impossible to tell if this is a complete sketch or a fragment, it is difficult to trace the sketch's earlier history, but it may have appeared in the following: Henri Cousin sale, 1841; J. Duclos sale, 1878; Marquiset sale, 1890 ["Fragment d'un tableau du maître," 50 x 26 cm].) LITERATURE: E. Munhall, "Quelques découvertes sur l'oeuvre de Greuze," *Revue du Louvre et des Musées de France,* XVI, 2, 1966, pp. 85–87.

The sketch may be a fragment of a larger sketch or simply a partial study for a composition. It shows a young maid, her body turned to the right while her head turns to the left in an expression of fearful astonishment. The earlier domestic tranquility of the scene is indicated by the large friendly cat, still purring happily as it stands on the table and rubs itself against the young girl's arm. Obviously the cat is not alarmed; the large mysterious hand that pokes in from the left is destined for the girl alone. That the source of the maiden's anxiety is invisible but for the hand points to the fragmentary character of the sketch, for Greuze was anecdotal in his pictures, and the figure of the man ought to be there. He does occur, however, in a lost picture by Greuze, *The Dishonest Proposals* (J. Martin, *Catalogue raisonné*, Pàris, 1908, No. 344), known only through an etching of 1786 by Watelet. The girl and the cat are both present, reversed and slightly altered, but the scene is now explicit: a lecherous old man clutches at the girl holding a purse while a small boy clutches at him and an old woman gestures in dismay. The girl in the etching, interestingly enough, is no longer alarmed, and while this may point to a change in interpretation, it may also mean that the sketch was made for a different picture, either *The Jealous Woman* or *The Surprised Housekeeper,* the latter also known to us from a Watelet etching of *ca.* 1765.

The style of the sketch and of the three possibly related pictures is characteristic of the busy surfaces and genre detail of Greuze's work of *ca.* 1760–1765. Here in the sketch Greuze shows his quick facility with the brush, a liveliness comparable with Hogarth's. The freshness and vibrancy have an immediacy and spontaneity that are lost in the smoother and more carefully executed final pictures.   D.M.

Lent by The Musée Grobet-Labadié, Marseilles

JEAN-HONORÉ FRAGONARD (1732–1806)

Born in Grasse, Fragonard received his first training in Paris, briefly under Chardin and then under Boucher with whom he had a greater affinity. Fragonard won the *Prix de Rome* and studied in Italy from 1756 to 1761. Upon his return to Paris he worked variously at landscapes, genre pictures, portraits, and erotic scenes. A more decorous historical subject earned him his entrance into the French Academy in 1765. Thereafter he gained the patronage of Louis XV and Mme. du Barry and in 1773 made another trip to Italy. Fragonard's career as a court painter ended in 1789, but during the next decade he was employed by revolutionary leaders to select works of art belonging to *emigré* noblemen for the museums of the Louvre and Versailles.

68. *SULTANA SEATED ON AN OTTOMAN.* Oil on canvas mounted on panel. 12¾ x 9⅞ inches (33 x 25 cm). COLLECTIONS: M(orel, etc.) sale, May 3, 1786; Wildenstein & Co.; E. A. Ball. LITERATURE: G. Wildenstein, *The Paintings of Fragonard,* London, 1960, No. 337.

This delightful little sketch represents the taste that swept through 18th-century Europe for the exotic, mysterious Near East as represented by Turkey. The *Sultana* sits low on a typically Turkish ottoman, enclosed in a room that hints of the harem, dressed in outlandish trousers. The oriental flavor of the milieu is transparent, but Fragonard endows the figure with French charm, giving her a pretty and doll-like face. He evidently had some difficulty in combining the Turkish crossed legs with a torso that rests in French fashion on a cushion, but the discrepancy is obscured by the costume. The treatment is still Rococo; henceforth French artists were never to lose their fascination for mysterious women from hot and foreign lands.

Wildenstein suggests that this sketch was done after a fairly large picture formerly in the Randon de Boisset collection, last sold in 1783 and now missing (Wildenstein, No. 338), but it seems much more likely that the sketch prepared the larger picture. The sketch may belong to the 1760's when Fragonard painted a number of fancy portraits and, in addition to the Randon de Boisset picture, used the sketch for a painting that is only slightly larger (Wildenstein, No. 336) and for a *Sultana,* half the size of these but more complete, for which he made a pendant *Sultan* (Wildenstein, Nos. 334, 335). E.V.

Lent by the Ball State University Art Gallery, Muncie, Indiana

69. *THE ITALIAN FAMILY.* Oil on canvas. 19¼ x 23⅜ inches (48.9 x 59.4 cm). Some retouching. COLLECTIONS: Hôtel Drouot, Paris, May 12, 1884, No. 21; G. Moreau-Chaslon, Paris; Charles Edward Haviland, Paris; O. Linet, 1918; Alfred Lowenstein, Brussels, 1930–1932; Howard Back, New York, 1946. LITERATURE: Charles Sterling, *The Metropolitan Museum of Art: A Catalogue of French Paintings, XV–XVIII Centuries,* Cambridge, 1955, p. 152 f; G. Wildenstein, *The Paintings of Fragonard,* London, 1960, No. 365.

Best remembered for his erotic subjects, Fragonard did not concentrate exclusively on them. While they were very popular in certain circles, in others he met with criticism for his frivolity of taste. Diderot at the time favored a more edifying approach to painting, exemplified by the art of Greuze. In keeping with this highly moral tone, Fragonard devoted himself to painting genre pictures, including such tender domestic scenes as *The Italian Family.* There are two other more finished versions of the composition, both called *Village Interior* or *The Happy Mother*, and both in private collections (Wildenstein, Nos. 363, 364). The sketch in the Metropolitan Museum would seem to be the first version, as a number of figures are still only adumbrated and the background has not yet been carefully defined. The figures emerge with more precision in Wildenstein No. 364, and in No. 363 Fragonard has defined the setting more clearly.

Inspiration for the composition and for the chiaroscuro effects may well have come partially from Rembrandt's painting of the *Holy Family* (Hermitage, Leningrad), which was in the Hôtel Crozat in Paris during the 18th century and which Fragonard had copied. Fragonard, who spent a long time in Bologna in 1761, may also have been influenced by the family groups of Giuseppe Maria Crespi, who also painted figures veiled in shadow, as may be seen in the two sketches shown in this exhibition (Nos. 2, 3). *The Italian Family* would probably have been painted in the years after Fragonard's first trip to Italy, although Wildenstein maintained that it was the fruit of his second voyage to Italy in 1773.   C.L.

Lent by The Metropolitan Museum of Art, New York, Dick Fund, 1946

70. *LA GIMBLETTE*. Oil on canvas. 24 x 30½ inches (61 x 77.5 cm). COLLECTIONS: Probably Villars (sale, March 13, 1868, No. 31) and Barroilhet (sale, March 16, 1872, No. 10). EXHIBITION: *The Age of the Rococo*, Residenz, Munich, 1958, No. 59. LITERATURE (primarily references to GIRL WITH A DOG): L. Réau, *Fragonard*, Brussels, 1956, p. 159; G. Wildenstein, *The Paintings of Fragonard*, London, 1960, Nos. 280–282; A. Ananoff, *L'Oeuvre dessiné de Jean-Honoré Fragonard*, Paris, 1961–1963, I, No. 107; II, No. 691.

This is probably the first oil sketch for a series of paintings with variations on the theme of a girl playing with a dog. A *gimblette* is a ring-shaped biscuit, which in this case the young lady uses to entice the dog, precariously balanced on her outstretched feet. Another dog emerging from beneath the bed is attracted to a string of biscuits that she dangles with her left hand. A number of painted replicas of this charming composition are known. Two slightly larger versions, formerly in the collections of E. Kraemer and G. Mühlbacher, are rendered with less forceful brushwork, variations in coloring, and minor iconographical changes, e.g. with the girl's left arm resting on the pillow and the dog under the bed removed. Ananoff cities a preparatory drawing for *La Gimblette* in pastel on gray paper, formerly in the collection of Camille Groult, Paris, together with a wash drawing of more dubious attribution. (There are also many engravings of the late 18th and 19th centuries after this composition; cf. Pl. 70A.)

Fragonard created a still larger canvas (89 x 70 cm) of a *Girl with a Dog* (Private Collection, Paris, Pl. 70B). This painting was erroneously called *La Gimblette* until it was noticed that there was no sign of a biscuit. In this larger painting, Fragonard has radically altered his original idea, seen in the sketch exhibited here, and has shown a more intimate stage in the relationship between the girl and the dog. The artist has changed her winsome smile into an ecstatic expression. In the Cailleux sketch the young lady wears a decorous blue-ribboned bonnet, which at the later stage has fallen off in the general excitement. Fragonard has almost entirely transformed the color scheme and, compared with the freely painted Cailleux sketch, the later work exhibits a more disciplined brushstroke.

Fragonard probably painted *La Gimblette* a few years after returning from his first trip to Italy, possibly as late as 1770. It has been suggested that before he was established as a court painter he started to paint boudoir scenes in order to earn money. Such amorous subjects were no longer always cloaked in mythological guise, which had been the practice since the Renaissance, and the playful and erotic character of the pictures under discussion speaks for itself. As in the case of *La Gimblette,* Fragonard often painted one subject in various stages, including such themes as the *Kiss* (lost, known now only through engravings) and the *Progress of Love* (Frick Collection, New York).

C.L.

Lent by M. Jean Cailleux, Paris

71. *HEAD OF A YOUNG MAN*. Oil on canvas. 17⅞ x 14¾ inches (46 x 38 cm). COLLECTIONS: Possibly the *Tête de Jeune Homme* in the Mme. de Cossé sale, November 11, 1778; Walferdin sale, April 12–16, 1880, No. 51; de Beurnonville sale, May 9–16, 1881, No. 70; Mme. Charras Collection. EXHIBITIONS: *Chefs-d'œuvre des Musées de province*, Musée de l' Orangerie, Paris, 1931, No. 17. LITERATURE: G. Wildenstein, *The Paintings of Fragonard*, London, 1960, No. 483; F. Boucher, "Fragonard," *Le Musée personnel*, Paris, 1966.

Late in the 1770's or early in the 1780's, Fragonard painted this head of an unknown young man. As the picture is executed with sparkling freedom of brushwork, it is difficult to tell whether it was intended as a study for another work or was itself a loose, informal portrait. In his portraits Fragonard generally sought spontaneity of expression rather than deep characterization or a precise likeness of the sitter. This exuberant young man bears some resemblance to the breathless youth in the painting of the *Fountain of Love* (Wallace Collection), signed and dated 1785, although the features of the young man in the later painting have been rather idealized.   C.L.

Lent by the Musée du Havre   Illustration facing Plate 58

72. *HEAD OF AN OLD MAN.* Oil on paper mounted on canvas. 16⅜ x 13¼ inches (41 x 33 cm). Signed: *frago.* COLLECTIONS: (de Ghendt) sale, 15 November, 1779, Lot 34, as *Tête de Vieillard, style de Rembrandt;* anon. sale, 30 January 1843, Lot 106; Barroilhet; Warneck sale, 27-28 May 1926, Lot 100; Wildenstein, New York. EXHIBITION: *Masterpieces of Art,* Cincinnati Art Museum, 1941, No. 19. LITERATURE: G. Wildenstein, *The Paintings of Fragonard,* London, 1960, No. 192.

This bold and brilliant sketch belongs to a series of about 20 *Têtes d'expression* painted *circa* 1763. In 1779 most of them were apparently owned by the engraver and dealer Emmanuel de Ghendt, who, according to Wildenstein (p. 11), had most probably commissioned them. But the group can by no means be considered a self-contained set. Nearly all show exclusively the head and clothed upper shoulders of an old man with features strikingly like those of the man here—a bony facial structure, balding forehead, humped nose, wide mouth, and flowing beard, moustache, and unkempt hair. But the group varies in the degree of finish, size, shape, and kind of support—paper, wood, and canvas were all used—, and so the series seems to be less a commissioned group on a set theme than a miscellany of private explorations of mood and expression. The interest in the revelation of character through external appearance, which has a long tradition behind it, was given a specific French impetus by the studies of Le Brun, and many 18th-century artists were equally fascinated by this semi-scientific problem. Fragonard combined his study of expression with stylistic experimentation, and the heads are painted in ways that reflect the styles of

Barocci and Guercino (Wildenstein) and, as Fragonard's contemporaries noted, of Tiepolo and Rembrandt. In this sketch it was certainly Rembrandt who engrossed Fragonard's mind, and the artist evokes the brooding intensity of the self-absorbed old man by a shimmering light that leaves the eyes and mouth in transitory shadow. The flicker of the brush and the quivering vitality of forms, however, are far from Rembrandt: these belong to Fragonard alone.   E.V.

Lent Anonymously   Illustration facing Plate 55

Germany and Austria

Attributed to JOHANN EVANGELIST HOLZER (1709-1740)

Holzer, born in the small town of Burgeis in southern Tyrol, went early to Augsburg, then the center of Bavaro-Swabian painting, where he trained with J. G. Bergmüller, a director of the Academy who had once studied in Rome with Maratti. His entire working career lasted only 10 years, but his virtuosity in manipulating light and shade with sculpturesque effects brought him an enormous following in Augsburg. A large part of his *œuvre* consisted of frescoes on house facades, which survive today mainly in his bozzetti.

73. *SKETCH FOR A CEILING DECORATION.* Oil on canvas. 21¾ x 38¼ inches (55.2 x 97.8 cm). COLLECTION: Hewitt (until 1931).

The attribution of this unpublished sketch is uncertain, depending on stylistic comparison with the known Holzer sketches for his architectural decorations in Augsburg. In them, as in this sketch, the structure of the composition is determined by architectural forms, organized on a mild curve, combined with highly articulated figures that are wedded to the architecture by the loose and airy lights and shadows. The dependence of the design on the fantastic, illusionist architecture reminds us of the influence Padre Pozzo had in the Austro-German world; his ideas on the perspective painting of architecture could have been known to Holzer through the 1719 German translation of Pozzo's *Perspectiva Pictorum et Architectorum,* first published in Rome in 1693. It is the reliance on the Pozzo-like architecture, as well as the use of a painting by Sebastiano Ricci (now in the Louvre) for the central group of figures, that suggests a date early in Holzer's career, perhaps *ca.* 1732.

The *sotto in sù* viewpoint and strong convergence of the architectural perspective demonstrate that this sketch is a preparation for a ceiling, extending the wall space of the room up into the heavens, similar to Pozzo's sketch for the ceiling of S. Ignazio (No. 14). Although the precise purpose of the sketch is unknown, the allegorical figures allow us to draw some conclusions. High in the center sits Minerva, goddess of Wisdom, intermediary between the celestial beings in a dome-like architecture above and the figure of Painting, holding a palette, who stands behind a balustrade below. At the bottom right Envy is cast out and at the top left the scythe of Time is carried away. Fame sounds her trumpet as on the left a noble figure is carried aloft. This figure, the coats-of-arms on the architecture, the emblematic figure at the bottom center, and the 'real' figures in contemporary dress who gaze upon the scene, all suggest that the subject is an allegorical compliment paid a noble patron who is elevated to eternal fame by his patronage of the arts, particularly the art of painting. This fantasy of light and color may well have been the youthful Holzer's offering to a patron, with the hope of winning an important commission.   D.M.

Lent by The Cooper Union Museum, New York

FRANZ ANTON MAULBERTSCH (1724–1796)

Born at Langenargen by Lake Constance, Maulbertsch was in Vienna by 1739 and two years later became a student at the Academy. In 1751 he took a first prize but had already been successful as a fresco painter. He remained in Vienna all his life, where he became the leading painter, famous for his expressive brush-stroke, sensitive colors, and fantastic imagination.

74. *SAINT JOHN OF NEPOMUK AS PATRON OF THE SICK AND POOR.* Oil on canvas. 22 x 13¾ inches (55 x 34.1 cm). COLLECTIONS: Harry Shaw Newman, 1928 (from Dr. Gottschalk's stock of The Old Print Shop); Victor D. Spark, New York, 1938; A. F. Mondschein, New York, 1939 (sold to The Wadsworth Atheneum, 1941). EXHIBITIONS: *Seventeenth and Eighteenth Century German Painting,* Fogg Art Museum, Harvard University, Cambridge, Mass., 1954; *German and Austrian Rococo Painting,* University of Kansas Museum of Art, Lawrence, Kansas, 1956, No. 18; *Homage to Mozart,* Wadsworth Atheneum, Hartford, 1956, No. 38; *The Age of Elegance: The Rococo and Its Effects,* Baltimore Museum of Art, 1959, No. 250. LITERATURE: *H. Schwarz,* "Franz Anton Maulbertsch in American Museums," *The Baltimore Museum of Art News,* XXIII, No. 1, 1959, pp. 13–14; K. Garas, *Franz Anton Maulbertsch, 1724–1796,* Graz, 1960, No. 129, and p. 244, Doc. XXII.

St. John Nepomuk, vicar-general of the archdiocese of Prague, was drowned in the Moldau in 1393 for resisting what he considered to be improper royal interference in church matters. Common belief held that he was killed for refusing to divulge the queen's confessional secrets, and his body, recovered from the river, became the focus of a local Bohemian cult that grew through the centuries. He was canonized in 1729, and his fame spread throughout the whole of central Europe.

This sketch is a study for a commission Maulbertsch received in May of 1760 for an altarpiece in the cathedral of Budweis (now Cĕské Budĕjovice), later transferred to the church of St. John Nepomuk in this same Czechoslovakian town of southern Bohemia. The sketch apparently won the patron's approval, for the altarpiece was ready only five months later. Although unfinished in such details as the corners, the quickly painted sketch gives a complete idea of the final composition. The weightless saint hovers at the center, interceding for the poor, sick, and dead below, while swirling angels float through the heavens above. The attenuated forms, subtly adjusted for vision from slightly below, give a mystic quality to the image, and the intercession theme appears almost transformed into a theme of the ascension from earthly misery to divine bliss. Accepting the dogmas of the Church with fervent belief, Maulbertsch was able to give them visual expression through his exalted fantasy, luminous colors, and shimmering lights.   D.M.

Lent by The Wadsworth Atheneum, Hartford: The Ella Gallup Sumner and Mary Catlin Sumner Collection

FRANZ SIGRIST THE ELDER (1727–1803)

Born at Alt-Breisach, Sigrist went to Vienna where he was a student of Paul Troger. In 1752 he took a second prize in painting at the Academy in Vienna, after which he traveled throughout Austria, Hungary, and southern Germany, working in fresco, oil, and etching. He shows the influence of Maulbertsch in the application of his paint but differs in setting gleaming highlights against somber backgrounds. His long career ended in Vienna where he died in 1803.

75. *ST. PETER DELIVERED FROM PRISON.* Oil on paper. 6¾ x 5¼ inches (17.2 x 13.3 cm). COLLECTIONS: Joseph Carl Ritter von Klinkosch, Vienna, 1822 (Wawra sale, 1889, No. 559, as Maulbertsch); Franz Trau, Vienna (Gilhofer and Ranschburg sale, 1934, No. 214, as Maulbertsch). EXHIBITIONS: *Entwürfe von Malern, Bildhauern und Architekten der Barockzeit in Österreich,* Vienna, 1937, No. 93 (as Johann Sigrist); *Exhibition of German and Austrian Painting of the Eighteenth Century,* University of Kansas Museum, Lawrence, 1956, No. 32 (as Johann Sigrist). LITERATURE: Mentioned in K. Garas, *Franz Anton Maulbertsch, 1724–1796,* Graz, 1960, p. 239 (under *Befreiung Petri*). (For Sigrist, see: O. Benesch, "Der Maler und Radierer Franz Sigrist," in *Festschrift zum sechzigsten Geburtstag von E. W. Braun,* Augsburg, 1931, pp. 185–197; brief notice in P. Preiss, "Der Barockmaler Franz Sigrist in der Prager Nationalgalerie," *Alte und moderne Kunst,* VIII, No. 69, 1963, pp. 12–17.)

The attribution of this sketch has in recent years been finally settled by stylistic comparison with Sigrist's known work. Typical of him are the fluid highlights and grey tonality, creating an air of dream-like fantasy. The dark atmosphere of gloomy and mysterious space acts as a foil for the light, which reveals the figures, models them, and creates the dynamic and excited tension between them. In his taste for bulky but weightless figures with exaggerated faces, Sigrist follows his teacher Maulbertsch, but Sigrist's harshness and angularities are entirely his own. He works here with few hesitancies, leaving such awkward forms as the putti uncorrected, and the sketch has the spontaneous freedom of a study dashed off in a very brief time. No finished picture related to our sketch is known, but the great mass of Sigrist's work is still unstudied and the altar or fresco execution may yet be discovered. A variant of the composition in the National Gallery in Prague may be an attendant study of the same date, *ca.* 1770–1780.   D.M.

Lent by Heinrich and Elisabeth Schwarz, Middletown, Connecticut

England

JAMES THORNHILL (1675/6–1734)

England's greatest Baroque history painter and decorator, Thornhill was born in Dorset and received his early training in London under Thomas Highmore. Thornhill broadened his experience by studying the works of Laguerre and Verrio and the Venetians Sebastiano Ricci and Pellegrini. In 1707 he was chosen over his foreign competitors to decorate the Painted Hall at Greenwich, and his success was made. For his most important public commission, the cupola of St. Paul's in London (1715–17), he painted eight large grisailles of scenes from the life of St. Paul, and in 1720 he was knighted by George I. When William Kent, protégé of the all-powerful Lord Burlington, won the commission to decorate Kensington Palace in 1722, Thornhill's popularity began to decline. He ended his years copying Raphael's cartoons at Hampton Court.

76. *TIME, VIGILANCE, AND PRUDENCE.* Oil on canvas. 9¾ x 19¼ inches (24.76 x 48.89 cm). COLLECTION: Dr. Alfred Scharf. LITERATURE: None. For Thornhill's life, see E. Croft-Murray, *Decorative Painting in England* (1537–1837), 1962, I, pp. 69–78.

77. *TIME, TRUTH, AND JUSTICE.* Oil on canvas. 9¾ x 19¼ inches (24.76 x 48.89 cm).

The intermingling of French and Italian influences in these sketches is peculiar to Thornhill's style and indicates his unique position in English art. His play of light and dark is Baroque in character, but Thornhill tempers this play with an even flow of forms and colors over the surface. The composition builds to no dramatic focus; on the contrary, Thornhill prefers well-populated scenes with a gentle ebullience throughout. According to a suggestion by Croft-Murray (unpublished), these two sketches, together with a third of the *Assemby of the Gods* (City Art Galleries, Manchester), were probably unexecuted projects for a staircase at Blenheim Palace (*circa* 1716). A great house such as Blenheim was typical of Thornhill's commissions, and the sketches are typical of his solutions for them: an easy combination of a decorative surface design with the language of myth and allegory.

Iconographically both sketches concern Time. In the first Father Time flies away to the left, leaving behind the mature results of his passage, Vigilance, with her book, lamp, and crane, and Prudence, gazing intently into her mirror. In the second, Father Time flies into the scene, revealing Truth with her Torch. The scene below is dominated by the crowned figure of Justice, holding her scales. Although the sketches are rich in attributes and personifications, the allegories are transparent in meaning. They may indeed even be alternatives for the same site, leaving the decision to the patron. Stylistically, however, they differ slightly. The first seems looser in structure and handling than the second, and the differences suggest that the second sketch is the later one. The history of the sketches is unknown, but they may have stayed with Thornhill until his death when his entire collection was sold at auction (T. Borenius, *Burlington Magazine,* LXXXII, 1943, pp. 133–6). D.W.P.

Lent by the Manchester City Art Galleries

WILLIAM HOGARTH (1697–1764)

Born in London, Hogarth received his early training as an engraver of arms on silver but struck out independently as a producer of prints and book illustrations. Forced by marriage to increase his income, he turned. apparently with little professional training, to portraits and conversation pieces. *The Wanstead Assembly* of 1729–31 established his reputation, and in the next decade he produced the great series of painted and engraved moral subjects for which he is best known. In 1745

Hogarth retired from society, embittered that his pictures were failing on the market, and worked out his aesthetic theories, published as the *Analysis of Beauty* in 1753. He later attempted to recapture his position, but met with little success in a world now dominated by Reynolds and Gainsborough.

79. *THE ILL EFFECTS OF MASQUERADES* (also called *THE SUICIDE OF THE COUNTESS*). Oil on canvas. 11¾ x 14⅝ inches (30 x 37 cm). Inscribed, lower left: *Willm Hogarth*. COLLECTIONS: Mrs. Hogarth; Samuel Ireland (traditionally believed to have been bought from Mrs. Hogarth, 1780); Peacock of Marylebone Street (until 1833); Chambers Hall (until 1855). EXHIBITIONS: Amsterdam, 1936, No. 69; *European Masters of the Eighteenth Century*, Royal Academy, London, 1954–55, No. 46. LITERATURE: Source material in J. Nichols, *Biographical Anecdotes of William Hogarth*, London, ed. 1781, p. 67*, ed. 1782, p. 102; and S. Ireland, *Graphic Illustrations of Hogarth*, London, 1799, II, pp. 98–101. For important later literature, with references, see C. F. Bell, "Three Sketches by Hogarth," *Burlington Magazine*, XLI, 1922, pp. 11–17; A. C. Sewter, "Some Early Works of Hogarth," *Burlington Magazine*, LXXX, 1942, pp. 5–10; *Paintings in the Ashmolean Museum*, Oxford, 1961, pp. 70–71; F. Antal, *Hogarth and His Place in European Art*, London, 1962, *passim*.

Opinions on the subject and purpose of this sketch have undergone a changing history. The sketch was first published by Ireland in 1799 with the explanation that it shows *The Ill Effects of Masquerades:* a husband, returning home unexpectedly at night, sees a man's costume on the floor and two figures in his bed, and stabs them both, only then learning that they were his wife and sister who had attended a masquerade as a gallant and his lady. Later the sketch was believed to represent *The Suicide of the Countess,* a rejected or early stage for the *Death of the Countess,* the sixth scene of *Marriage à la Mode.* Another student saw in the sketch a study for the seventh scene in *The Rake's Progress,* where the forsaken mistress faints on recognizing her faithless lover. And still another went so far as to see two separate groups on the left and right sides of the sketch, two variations of the same theme (Bell, pp. 16–17). Yet there is no doubt that the sketch shows a single theme, and the very fact that the sketch could be related to the *Marriage à la Mode* and *The Rake's Progress* shows that the relationships are casual, based on the motif of the swooning woman. Antal quite correctly returned to the 18-century source, and the scene almost certainly illustrates *The Ill Effects of Masquerades,* to be dated stylistically to *circa* 1740–45.

The confusion in identifying the scene points up the extraordinary freedom of the sketch, the translation of the subject into almost abstract patches of color that often only hint at the forms. Hogarth evidently never developed this sketch beyond this stage, but the composition's structure is already clear and strong in the sweeping diagonals against the planar walls. Hogarth corrects himself as he paints, altering the man at the center as his brush flies across the surface. The unusual boldness and economy are striking in their immediacy and accomplishment, and the freedom of the liquid brush anticipates and even surpasses the vigor and dynamism we later meet in Delacroix.   D.W.P.

Lent by the Visitors of the Ashmolean Museum, Oxford

78. *THE ENRAGED MUSICIAN*. Oil on canvas. 14¾ x 18¾ inches (38 x 48 cm). COLLECTIONS: Mrs. Hogarth; Samuel Ireland (bought 1780; Christie's sale, May 7, 1801); Anon. (Christie's sale, June 18, 1805, lot 63); Anon. (Christie's sale, March 12, 1825, lot 95); Chambers Hall. EXHIBITIONS: Whitechapel, London, 1906, No. 142; *British Art,* Royal Academy, London, 1934, No. 59; *Twee Eeuwen Engelsche Kunst,* Amsterdam, 1936, No. 66; *Hogarth,* Tate Gallery, London, 1951, No. 43; *Hogarth,* Manchester, 1954, No. 28. LITERATURE: P. Pindar, "Original Anecdotes of Hogarth," *Gentleman's Magazine,* LV, 1785, pp. 346–347; R. B. Beckett, *Hogarth,* London, 1949, p. 65; *Paintings in the Ashmolean Museum,* Oxford, 1961, p. 70; F. Antal, *Hogarth and His Place in European Art,* London, 1962, *passim.* (For the print, see F. G. Stephens, *Catalogue of Prints and Drawings in the British Museum, Div. I: Political and Personal Satires,* III, Part I, London, 1877, Nos. 2517–2527; and R. Paulson, *Hogarth's Graphic Works,* New Haven, 1965, I, pp. 184–186.)

This monochrome sketch illustrates an aspect of artistic activity that had a long tradition in the art of Northern Europe, the painting of an oil sketch in preparation for a print (Pl. 78A). In this case there can be no doubt about Hogarth's intentions, because the little drummer-boy was sketched in reverse so that he would turn out playing normally in the engraving and because Hogarth himself announced the print's publication. In the *London Daily Post* of November 24, 1740, he advertised *The Enraged Musician* as a companion piece to a print he had already made, *The Distressed Poet,* both of which were to be followed by an engraving concerned with the painter, never in fact produced.

The sketch is supposedly based on an anecdote told to the artist by a clergyman (Pindar, pp. 346–347). A music teacher was playing at an open window while waiting for his pupil to get up; outside a man with a barrow of onions offered a street-musician to exchange an onion for a tune; when the transaction was happily concluded and about to be repeated, the violinist at the window became enraged at this prostitution of art. There have even been attempts to give reality to the story by identifying the musician—originally as a Mr. John Festin, then as Cervetto, a bass player in the London theatres, as Castrucci, the leader of Handel's orchestra, or as Thomas Arne, the composer of *Rule Britannia*. But all of these are of course beside the point. The real subject is the amusing contrast between high art and low art, between the practitioner of the noble and learned art of the violin and the vulgar hawkers of common music. And indeed the street scene teems with bustling, noisy life, present in the sketch and added to in the engraving: shrieking children, shouting peddlers, a whining knife-grinder, a tinny oboe-player, a yapping dog, a drumming child, and a water-making little boy.

This presentation of clamorous street-life is so animate and vital that we feel Hogarth must simply have looked out his window for his models, and of course their striking realism does depend on sharp, precise observation. But the accumulation of peddlers and street-criers in teeming variety reminds us that Hogarth was working in a specific tradition of cycles of prints of everyday life. *The Cries of London* were popular already in the 17th century, and Hogarth certainly knew the prints of the *Cris de Paris* of his French contemporaries, in particular the engravings made from the designs of Boucher and Bouchardon. For all its seeming randomness and spontaneity of touch Hogarth's sketch represents a careful selection of types, and their expansion in number from sketch to print was equally discriminating. Hogarth's famous *Shrimp Girl* (London, National Gallery) is a sketch either for the milkmaid in this engraving or for the fisherwoman in *Beer Street* (1751).

The Enraged Musician was enormously popular. Hogarth himself re-printed it several times with minor variations, it was copied by others, and in 1789 the playwright Colman adapted it into a pantomime, under the title of *Ut Pictura Poesis; or, the Enraged Musician,* the last tableau of which reproduced the print.   D.W.P.

Lent by the Visitors of the Ashmolean Museum, Oxford

Plates

1. Annibale Caracci, *Head of a Man in Profile* (17⅝ x 12⅝ inches). The Royal Collections, Hampton Court Palace.

2. G. M. Crespi, *Blind Beggar* (14⅜ x 10⅝ inches). Pilati Collection, Bologna.

3. G. M. Crespi, *Peasant Scene with Street Musicians* ($18\frac{5}{8}$ x $12\frac{3}{4}$ inches). Claflin Collection, New York.

4A. G. M. Crespi, *The Martyrdom of St. Peter of Arbués.* Altarpiece in the Collegio di Spagna, Bologna. Oil on canvas, 1733-39. (*Not in exhibition.*)

4. G. M. Crespi, *The Martyrdom of St. Peter of Arbués* (16½ x 11 inches). Pinacoteca Nazionale, Bologna.

5. Gaetano Gandolfi. *Rape of Ganymede* (15 x 19½ inches). Ford Collection, London.

6. *Attributed to* Gianlorenzo Bernini, *A Boy Singing* (10 1/16 x 9⅜ inches). Glasgow University.

7. Andrea Sacchi, *Madonna and Child with Saints* (24 x 15¾ inches). Sewell Collection, London.

8. P. F. Mola, *Carthusians in a Landscape* (13¾ x 18 inches). Busiri Vici Collection, Rome.

9. P. F. Mola, *Franciscans in a Landscape* (14¼ x 18 inches). Busiri Vici Collection, Rome.

10. Salvator Rosa, *Pindar and Pan* (39⅛ x 29 inches). Lewine Collection, New York.

11. Filippo Lauri, *Autumn and Winter* (15 x 25¾ inches). Humphris Collection, London.

12. Attributed to G. P. Schorr, *Mermaids and Tritons* (15¼ x 20¼ inches). The Cooper Union Museum.

13. G. B. Gaulli, *The Four Doctors of the Latin Church* (29 x 26½ inches). The Ponce Art Museum.

14. Andrea Pozzo, *Allegory of the Missionary Work of the Jesuits* (69½ x 135¼ inches). Galleria Nazionale, Rome.

15. G. P. Panini, *Festival in the Piazza Navona* (10⅝ x 18 inches). The Art Institute of Chicago.

15A. G. P. Panini, *Festival in the Piazza Navona*, 1731. Oil on canvas (42½ x 98½ inches). National Gallery of Ireland. (*Not in exhibition.*)

16. Francesco Mancini, *St. Philip Neri in Ecstasy* (38½ x 26 inches). Galleria Nazionale, Rome.

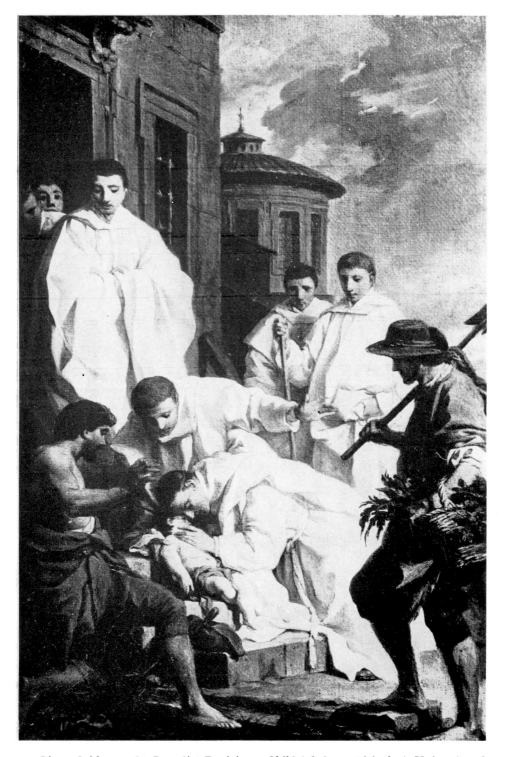

17. Pierre Subleyras, *St. Benedict Reviving a Child* (16¼ x 10¾ inches). University of North Carolina.

18. Pompeo Batoni, *Allegory of the Arts* (11⅝ x 8⅞ inches). Busiri Vici Collection, Rome.

19. Giuseppe Cades, *The Story of Count Gautier* (4½ x 9¼ inches). Ford Collection, London.

19A. Giuseppe Cades, *The Story of Count Gautier*. Oil sketch on canvas (14⅝ x 27½ inches) *ca.* 1787. The Art Institute of Chicago. *(Not in exhibition.)*

19B. Giuseppe Cades, *The Story of Count Gautier,* ceiling fresco in the Villa Borghese, Rome. *ca.* 1787. *(Not in exhibition.)*

20. Bernardo Cavallino, *Saint Cecilia* (24 x 19½ inches). Museo di Capodimonte, Naples.

21. Mattia Preti, *The Martyrdom of St. Catherine* (40 x 29$\frac{9}{16}$ inches). Manning Collection, New York.

22. Luca Giordano, *St. Luke Painting the Virgin* (18⅛ x 14¼ inches). Busiri Vici Collection, Rome.

23. Giacomo del Po, *Palazzo Mattei Ceiling Sketch* (40⅛ x 23⅝ inches). Museo di S. Martino, Naples.

24. Francesco Solimena, *St. Vincent Ferrer* (28 x 22⅝ inches). Viezzoli Collection, Genoa.

25. Francesco De Mura, *The Investiture of Carloman* (24¼ x 18¼ inches). Lewine Collection, New York.

26. Bernardo Strozzi, *Horatius Cocles Defending the Bridge* (9½ x 14 inches). Mahon Collection, London.

27. Valerio Castello, *Tobias and The Angel* (48½ x 21½ inches). Private Collection.

28. G. B. Castiglione, *Shepherd and Flocks* (10½ x 18½ inches). The Royal Library, Windsor Castle.

29. G. B. Castiglione, *Christ on the Cross* (10⅜ x 15½ inches). The Royal Library, Windsor Castle.

30. Tanzio da Varallo, *The Battle of Sennacherib* (59 x 36 inches). The Banca Popolare of Novara.

30A. Tanzio da Varallo, *The Battle of Sennacherib*. Oil on canvas (228 x 104 inches). 1627-29. S. Gaudenzio, Novara. *(Not in exhibition.)*

31. Alessandro Magnasco, *Dying Soldier* (20 x 11 inches). Pinacoteca
Malaspina, Padua.

32. Alessandro Magnasco, *Burial of a Soldier* (20 x 11 inches). Pinacoteca Malaspina, Padua.

33. Carlo Carloni, *The Sacrifice of Iphegenia* (16¾ x 27½ inches). Rust Collection, Washington.

34. Carlo Carloni, *God the Father Receiving the Madonna of the Immaculate Conception* (38¾ x 30⁵⁄₁₆ inches). The Smithsonian Institution.

35. Giuseppe Bazzani, *A Body Carried to its Grave* (24½ x 15 inches). Kress Collection, New York.

36. Giuseppe Bazzani, *A Soul led to Heaven by an Angel* (24½ x 15 inches). Kress Collection, New York.

37. Domenico Fetti, *David* (20 x 15 inches). Viezzoli Collection, Genoa.

38. Sebastiano Ricci, *Assumption of the Virgin* (54¾ x 28¼ inches).
Museum of Fine Arts, Springfield.

39. G. B. Pittoni, *The Sacrifice of Isaac* (5⅛ x 7 inches). Ganz Collection, New York.

39A. G. B. Pittoni, *The Sacrifice of Isaac*. Oil on canvas, *ca.* 1718-21. S. Francesco della Vigna, Venice. *(Not in exhibition.)*

40. G. A. Pellegrini, *Jezebel Inducing Ahab to Worship Baal* (6 x 7¼ inches). Scholz Collection, New York.

41. G. B. Piazzetta, *The Guardian Angel* (26 x 18½ inches). Los Angeles County Museum of Art.

42. G. B. Tiepolo, *Temptation of St. Anthony* (15¾ x 18½ inches). Pinacoteca di Brera.

43. G. B. Tiepolo, *Apotheosis of Aenaeas* (27½ x 19¼ inches). The Fogg Art Museum.

44. G. B. Tiepolo, *Neptune and the Winds* (24½ x 24½ inches). Metropolitan Museum of Art.

45. Canaletto, *Figure Studies* (15⅞ x 23 inches). London Collection.

46. Gianantonio Guardi. *Athena Dictating Laws to Odysseus* (?) (13¾ x 15¾ inches). Musée de Picardie, Amiens.

47. Peter Paul Rubens, *St. Gregory of Nazianzus* (19¾ x 25¾ inches). The Albright-Knox Art Gallery.

48. Peter Paul Rubens, *Elijah* (12¾ x 17¾ inches). Baer Collection, New York.

50. Peter Paul Rubens. *Meeting of the Two Ferdinands* (19 x 24¾ inches). Kramarsky Collection, New York.

52. Jacob Jordaens, *Telemachus Leads Theoclymenus to his Mother Penelope* (11⅛ x 20⅛ inches). Nationalmuseum, Stockholm.

51. Jacob Jordaens, *Head of Abraham Grapheus* (26½ x 20½ inches). The Detroit Institute of Arts.

53. Anthony van Dyck, *Betrayal of Christ* (55 x 44½ inches). The Minneapolis Institute of Arts.

54. Anthony van Dyck, *Man Wearing a Falling Ruff* (20¼ x 18 inches). The Ashmolean Museum.

54A. Anthony van Dyck, *The Magistrates of Brussels*. Oil sketch on panel (10½ x 23⅜ inches), *circa* 1634. Ecole des Beaux-Arts, Paris. *(Not in exhibition.)*

55. Rembrandt van Rijn, *Head of an Old Man with a Beard* ($9\frac{1}{2}$ x $7\frac{1}{2}$ inches). Whitney Collection, New York.

72. J.-H. Fragonard, *Head of an Old Man* (16⅜ x 13¼ inches). Private Collection.

56. Charles Le Brun, *Allegory of the Capture of Ghent* (25¼ x 41¾ inches). Musée des Beaux-Arts, Troyes.

57. Charles de La Fosse, *The Rising of the Sun* (39 inches in diameter). Musée des Beaux-Arts, Rouen.

58. Hyacinthe Rigaud, *Portrait of the Duc d'Estrées* (20½ x 16⅛ inches). Smith College Museum of Art.

71. J.-H. Fragonard, *Head of a Young Man* (17⅞ x 14¾ inches). Musée du Havre.

59. F.-A. Desportes, *Cloud Study* (11$\frac{7}{16}$ x 13 inches). Manufacture Nationale de Sèvres.

59A. F.-A. Desportes, *Landscape Study*. Oil on cardboard (12⅜ x 20 inches). Musée National de Compiègne. (*Not in exhibition.*)

60. François Boucher, *Pêche chinoise* (15⅞ x 18¾ inches). Musée des Beaux-Arts, Besançon.

61. François Boucher, *Chasse chinoise* (15¾ x 18¾ inches). Musée des Beaux-Arts, Besançon.

62. François Boucher, *The Abduction of Proserpina* (22⅝ x 18¾ inches). Musée de la Ville de Quimper.

63. François Boucher, *Danaë* (11⅜ x 13¾ inches). Nationalmuseum, Stockholm.

63A. François Boucher, *Danaë Receiving the Golden Shower.* Chalk drawing, dated 1757. National Gallery of Art, Washington, D. C., Samuel H. Kress Collection. *(Not in exhibition.)*

64. J.-F. de Troy, *The Capture of the Golden Fleece* (21¾ x 31¾ inches). Hodgkin Collection, London.

64A. J.-F. de Troy, *Jason and the Golden Fleece*. Gobelins tapestry, 1743. Victoria and Albert Museum. *(Not in exhibition.)*

65. Jean Barbault, *St. Jerome in the Desert* (13⅜ x 8³⁄₁₆ inches). Busiri Vici Collection, Rome.

66. J.-M. Vien, *An Invocation Scene* (11⅜ x 8¼ inches). Musée des Beaux-Arts, Rouen.

67. J.-B. Greuze, *The Surprised Housekeeper* (19$\frac{11}{16}$ x 10$\frac{3}{16}$ inches). Musée Grobet-Labadié, Marseille.

68. J.-H. Fragonard, *Sultana Seated on an Ottoman* (12¾ x 9⅞ inches). The Ball State University sity Art Gallery.

70. J.-H. Fragonard, *La Gimblette* (24 x 30½ inches). Cailleux Collection. Paris.

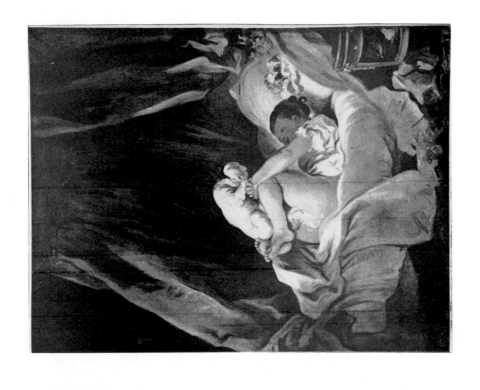

70A. J.-H. Fragonard, *La Gimblette*. Engraving of 1783 by Bertoni after the lost original. (*Not in exhibition.*)

70B. J.-H. Fragonard, *Girl Making Her Dog Dance on Her Bed*. Oil on canvas (35⅝ x 28 inches). Private Collection, Paris. (*Not in exhibition.*)

69. J.-H. Fragonard, *The Italian Family* (19¼ x 23⅜ inches). The Metropolitan Museum of Art.

73. *Attributed to J. E. Holzer, Sketch for a Ceiling Decoration* (21¾ x 38¼ inches). The Cooper Union Museum.

74. F. A. Maulbertsch, *St. John Nepomuk as Patron of the Sick and Poor* (22 x 13¾ inches). The Wadsworth Athenaeum.

75. Franz Sigrist the Elder, *St. Peter Delivered from Prison* (6¾ x 5¼ inches). Schwarz Collection, Middletown, Conn.

76. James Thornhill, *Time, Vigilance and Prudence* (9¾ x 19¼ inches). Manchester City Art Galleries.

77. James Thornhill, *Time, Truth and Justice* (9¾ x 19¼ inches). Manchester City Art Galleries.

78. William Hogarth, *The Enraged Musician* (14¾ x 18¾ inches). The Ashmolean Museum.

78A. William Hogarth, *The Enraged Musician*. Engraving, third state (13¹⁄₈ x 15¹⁄₈ inches). Signed and dated November 30, 1741. (*Not in exhibition.*)

79. William Hogarth, *The Ill Effects of Masquerades* (11¾ x 14⅝ inches). The Ashmolean Museum.